FURTHER *Curriculum Bank*

S

NUMBER

KEY STAGE TWO/ SCOTTISH LEVELS C–E

RICHARD ENGLISH

Published by Scholastic Ltd,
Villiers House,
Clarendon Avenue,
Leamington Spa,
Warwickshire CV32 5PR
Text © Richard English
© 1999 Scholastic Ltd
1234567890 9012345678

Author
Richard English

Editor
Kate Pearce

Assistant Editor
Roanne Davis

Series designer
Rachel Warner

Designer
Mark Udall

Illustrations
Tony O'Donnell

Cover illustration
Lesley Saddington

Scottish 5–14 links
Margaret Scott and Susan Gow

Acknowledgements
© **Crown copyright 1995**. Material from the National
Curriculum, Scottish 5–14 Guidelines and the Northern
Ireland Curriculum is reproduced by permission of the
Controller of Her Majesty's Stationery Office.
**Her Majesty's Stationery Office and the Department for
Education and Employment** for the use of extracts from
The National Numeracy Strategy: *Framework for Teaching
Mathematics* © March 1999, Crown Copyright
A.C. Cooper for photographs of the front cover illustrations
© 1999, A.C. Cooper

British Library Cataloguing-in-Publication Data
A catalogue record for this book is available from
the British Library.

ISBN 0-590-53874-8

Contents

Introduction

The importance of numeracy

There are few people in our society who would not subscribe to the view that numeracy is an essential life-skill and so should be afforded great importance at all levels of education. This is particularly true in the early years, indeed it should be the right of every child to become numerate by the time they leave primary school. It is therefore absolutely correct that number work occupies a large proportion of time in the early years to such an extent that 'number' is often synonymous with 'mathematics'. However, it is important that we do not place too narrow a definition on 'number' or 'numeracy'. Both are concerned with much more than just basic arithmetic. Number work involves an understanding of the number system and place value, an awareness of the patterns and relationships which exist between numbers, as well as a knowledge of various computational skills. Finally, let us not forget that the whole purpose of learning about number is so that we can use and apply what we have learned. Pupils should therefore spend a large amount of time using and applying their number skills to solve problems, to handle data, and to measure various aspects of the world around them. It is because number work reaches out into all of these areas that numeracy is such an important skill for life.

About this book

This book provides a bank of activities which are designed to help children to develop knowledge, skills and

understanding in number. The activities can easily be incorporated into any existing mathematics scheme of work and can be used in conjunction with other published resources. They have been designed to support the *Framework for Teaching Mathematics* by incorporating several key features:

A strong emphasis on whole-class teaching: Every lesson starts with a whole-class, teacher-led introduction and concludes in the same way. The intention is that all pupils in the class will be doing mathematics at the same time, although during the main activity there is the opportunity for different groups of pupils to do slightly different tasks according to ability.

A strong emphasis on interactive teaching: The teacher plays a key role in every lesson and acts as much more than simply a facilitator or passive observer. The teacher is expected to interact with the pupils throughout the lesson, particularly when working with the whole class during the introduction and plenary. Here, the interaction is stimulated by asking appropriate questions to encourage the pupils to think about, explain and discuss mathematics. Every activity identifies key questions the teacher must ask to facilitate effective interaction with the pupils.

A strong emphasis on developing mental skills: Many activities focus on the development, reinforcement and practise of mental skills. Even if this is not the main focus, the interaction with pupils during the introduction and plenary is often used for quick-fire mental practice.

Lesson plans

The structure for each activity is as follows.

Activity title box
The box at the beginning of each activity outlines the following key aspects:

Learning objective

These learning objectives break down aspects of the programmes of study for Mathematics and the *Framework for Teaching Mathematics* into manageable teaching and learning chunks, and their purpose is to aid planning for progression. These objectives can easily be referenced to the National Curriculum and Scottish 5–14 requirements by using the overview grid on pages 7 to 12. The learning objectives are appropriately focused thus allowing judgements to be made about pupil progress at the end of each activity.

Class organization/Likely duration

Icons ♦♦ and ⊕ signpost the suggested structure and group sizes for each activity and the approximate amount of time required to complete it. Nearly all of the activities begin with a whole-class introduction and conclude with a whole-class plenary but there is much variety in the organisation of the main part of the lesson.

Previous skills/knowledge needed

Information is given here when it is necessary for the children to have acquired specific knowledge or skills prior to carrying out the activity.

Key background information

This section outlines the areas of study covered by each activity and gives a general background to the particular topic or theme, outlining the basic skills that will be developed and the way in which the activity will address children's learning.

Preparation

Advice is given for those occasions when it is necessary for the teacher to prime the pupils for the activity or to prepare materials, or to set up a visual aid prior to the lesson.

Resources needed

All materials needed to carry out the activity are listed here.

What to do

Easy-to-follow, step-by-step instructions are given for carrying out the activity, including suggested questions for the teacher to ask pupils to help instigate discussion and stimulate investigation. These instructions are conveniently divided into three sections; introduction, main activity and plenary.

Suggestion(s) for extension/support

In these sections, suggestions are given for ways of providing differentiation.

Assessment opportunities

Where appropriate, opportunities for ongoing teacher assessment of the children's work during or after a specific activity are highlighted.

Opportunities for IT

Where opportunities for IT would strengthen an activity, these are briefly outlined with reference to particularly suitable types of program.

Display ideas

Where they are relevant and innovative, display ideas are incorporated into activity plans and illustrated with examples.

Reference to photocopiable sheets

Where activities include photocopiable activity sheets, small reproductions of these are included in the lesson plans together with guidance notes for their use and, where appropriate, suggested answers. Where appropriate, reference is also made to the photocopiable sheet in the *Preparation* section.

Overview Grid

This grid helps you to track the coverage of the Programme of Study for Maths at Key Stage Two, or the Scottish National Guidelines for Mathematics 5–14 at Levels C–E, offered by the activities in this book. For each activity, the relevant statements from the National Curriculum for England and Wales and the Scottish 5–14 Guidelines are indicated (the latter references are given in italics).

Most of the activities in this book can be used alongside the activities in the *Curriculum Bank for Number at Key Stage Two/ Scottish Levels C–E*. These links are indicated by the notes in the shaded panel below the relevant activities. The National Numeracy Strategy (NNS) section in this grid shows how the activities relate to the key objectives set out in the Numeracy Framework. The page references refer to the supplement of examples, so that, for example, Y3 p9 indicates Year 3 page 9.

ACTIVITY TITLE	LEARNING OBJECTIVE	POS/AO	NNS	CONTENT	PAGE
Place value dice games	To understand that the position of a digit affects its value. To practise mental addition skills involving two-digit numbers.	N 2a understand that the position of a digit signifies its value. N 3d develop a variety of mental methods of computation with whole numbers up to 100. *Addition, level C*	Know what each digit in a number represents (Y3 p9; Y4/5/6 p2–3). Understand the operation of addition (Y3 p24–25; Y4/5/6 p34–35). Add a pair of numbers mentally (Y3 p36–41; Y4/5/6 p44–47).	Various dice games to reinforce place value. Games played with whole class and in pairs.	13
Big, bigger, biggest, p14					
Tens, hundreds and thousands	To be able to multiply and divide by 10, 100, 1000 etc.	N 2a multiply and divide by powers of 10 when there are whole-number answers. *Multiply and divide, level D*	Multiply and divide whole numbers by 10, 100 or 1000 (Y4/5/6 p6–7).	Pupils roll two dice and carry out the multiplication or division indicated by the scores. Game played in pairs.	16
Moving digits, page 16					
Fractions with pattern blocks	To demonstrate an understanding of fractions through shape-filling activities.	N 2c understand and use fractions. *Fractions, level C*	Recognise and use simple fractions (Y3 p20–23; Y4/5/6 p22–23).	Pupils must fill a certain fraction of a shape with pattern blocks of a particular colour. Individual practical activity.	18
Piece by piece, page 22					
Congruent halves	To apply knowledge of simple fractions. To understand the concept of congruence.	N 2c understand and use fractions. SS & M 2c understand the congruence of simple shapes. *As above*	Describe and use simple fractions (Y3 p20–23; Y4/5/6 p22–23). Describe and visualise 2-D shapes (Y4/5/6 p102–103).	Reinforcement of basic principles of fractions by dividing shapes into halves, thirds, quarters etc but with the added challenge that all pieces must be congruent. Individual photocopiable sheet activity.	21
Multilink make half	To understand the concept of 'half'. To apply this in a practical investigation.	U & A 4b search for pattern in their results. U & A 4c make general statements. N 2c understand and use fractions. *Fractions, level B*	Recognise and use simple fractions (Y3 p20–23; Y4/5/6 p22–23). Recognise and explain patterns, generalise and predict (Y3 p62–63; Y4/5/6 p78–79).	Pupils make cuboids from multilink so that each face is half of one colour and half of another. They must investigate for which numbers of multilink this is possible. Practical investigative activity in small groups.	23
Round and round	To round decimals to the nearest whole number.	N 2a approximate numbers. N 2b extend their understanding of the number system to decimals. *Round numbers, level E*	Round decimal fractions to the nearest whole number (Y4/5/6 p30–31).	Number track game in which complex decimal answers are generated using a calculator and then rounded to the nearest whole number. Game played in pairs or small groups.	25
How high can you go?, page 17					

ACTIVITY TITLE	LEARNING OBJECTIVE	POS/AO	NNS	CONTENT	PAGE
Multilink primes	To understand prime numbers and factors. To find prime numbers through a practical investigation involving multiplication.	N 3a use some properties of numbers, including multiples, factors and squares, extending to primes. *Patterns and sequences, level E*	Recognise prime numbers and identify factors (Y4/5/6 p20–21).	Pupils are introduced to prime numbers through an investigative practical activity. Individual practical activity.	28
Number properties, page 53; Special numbers, page 99					
Set search	To identify numbers which belong to a particular set or sequence eg multiples, factors, primes, square numbers, triangular numbers.	N 3a use some properties of numbers, including multiples, factors and squares, extending to primes. *As above*	Recognise odd and even numbers, multiples, square numbers, prime numbers, and identify factors (Y4/5/6 p18–21).	Various sets and sequences of numbers are arranged horizontally, vertically and diagonally on a grid. Pupils must identify these sets and sequences. Individual worksheet-based activity.	30
Number properties, page 53; Special numbers, page 99					
Ups and downs	To quickly identify numbers which belong to a particular set or sequence.	N 3a use some properties of numbers, including multiples, factors and squares, extending to primes. *As above*	Recognise odd and even numbers, multiples, square numbers, prime numbers, and identify factors (Y4/5/6 p18–21).	Snakes and ladders type game but special numbers are used to indicate the snakes and ladders eg land in a square number and you move on to the next square number, land on a prime number and you move back to the previous prime number. Game in pairs or small groups.	31
Fibonacci towers	To follow simple rules to generate number sequences. To identify and explain the patterns in number sequences.	U & A 4b search for pattern in their results. N 3a explore number sequences, explaining patterns and using simple relationships. *As above*	Recognise and explain patterns and relationships, generalise and predict (Y4/5/6 p78–79).	Pupils investigate various properties of the Fibonacci Sequence and other similar sequences. Individual photocopiable sheet-based activity.	33
Fibonacci numbers, page 48					
Palindromes	To understand the meaning of palindrome. To identify numbers which belong to a particular set or sequence. To use the facilities of a calculator effectively to investigate special numbers.	N 3a use some properties of numbers, including multiples, factors and squares, extending to primes. N 3h understand and use the features of a basic calculator. *As above*	Recognise mulitples, square numbers and prime numbers (Y4/5/6 p18–21). Develop calculator skills and use a calculator effectively (Y4/5/6 p70–71). Solve mathematical problems (Y4/5/6 p78–79).	Pupils are introduced to palindromes and then must find palindromes with particular characteristics based on special numbers eg find a palindrome which is prime, which is a multiple of 12. Individual photocopiable sheet-based activity.	35
Maths with a calendar	To identify patterns and relationships in number grids. To practise mental and pencil and paper arithmetic skills.	U & A 4b search for pattern in their results. U & A 4c make general statements. N 3a explore number sequences, explaining patterns and using simple relationships. N 3d develop a range of non-calculator methods of computation. *Patterns and sequences, level E*	Solve mathematical problems, recognise and explain patterns and relationships, generalise and predict (Y4/5/6 p78–79). Make and investigate a general statement (Y4/5/6 p80–81).	Pupils investigate various properties, patterns and relationships involving numbers arranged on a calendar. Individual photocopiable sheet-based activity.	37

ACTIVITY TITLE	LEARNING OBJECTIVE	POS/AO	NNS	CONTENT	PAGE
NUMBER					
Neighbours	To identify patterns in sums of consecutive numbers. To add two or more numbers up to 100 without a calculator.	N 3a explore number sequences, explaining patterns and using simple relationships. N 3d develop a range of non-calculator methods of computation. *Addition, level D*	Add a pair of numbers or several numbers (Y4/5/6 p42–47). Solve mathematical problems, recognise and explain patterns and relationships, generalise and predict (Y4/5/6 p78–79).	Pupils investigate patterns or pairs which arise when two or more consecutive numbers are added together. Individual investigative activity.	40
Matchstick patterns	To identify and continue visual patterns. To generate and continue number sequences associated with a visual pattern.	U & A 4b search for pattern in their results. N 3a explore number sequences, explaining patterns and using simple relationships. *Patterns and sequences, level D*	Recognise and explain patterns and relationships (Y4/5/6 p78–79).	Pupils identify the patterns in arrangements of matchsticks and then continue these patterns. The next stage is to investigate the numerical patterns and sequences associated with the matchsticks. Individual activity.	42
Seeing squares, page 29					
Zoom	To follow a set of instructions shown on a flow-chart. To use a calculator effectively. To identify number patterns in sets of results.	U & A 4b search for pattern in their results. N 3a explore number sequences, explaining patterns and using simple relationships. N 3h understand and use the features of a basic calculator. *Functions and equations, level D*	Develop calculator skills and use a calculator effectively (Y4/5/6 p70–71). Recognise and explain patterns and relationships (Y4/5/6 p78–79).	Pupils use a calculator to work through a flow-chart to produce an answer. There is a relationship between rhe numbers used in the flow-chart and the final anser produced. Pupils must investigate this relationship. Individual investigative activity.	45
Twelve square centimetres	To draw shapes of a given area. To identify patterns and relationships in the numerical properties of shapes.	U & A 4b search for pattern in their results. U & A4c make general statements. N 3a explore number sequences, explaining patterns and using simple relationships; progress to generalising. SS & M 4c find areas by counting methods. *Range of shapes, level D*	Solve mathematical problems, recognise and explain patterns and relationships (Y4/5/6 p78–79). Measure and calculate the area of simple shapes (Y4/5/6 p96–97).	Pupils draw shapes of a given area on spotty paper and then investigate numerical patterns based on the properties of these shapes. Individual investigative activity.	48
The painted cube	To identify and explain numerical patterns and relationships. To make predictions based on numerical patterns.	U & A 4b search for pattern in their results. U & A 4c make general statements. N 3a explore number sequences, explaining patterns and using simple relationships; progress to interpreting, generalising and using simple mappings. *Patterns and sequences, level C*	Solve mathematical problems, recognise and explain patterns and relationships, generalise and predict (Y4/5/6 p78–79).	Pupils investigate numerical patterns and relationships based on the properties of cubes of various sizes. Practical activity in pairs.	51

ACTIVITY TITLE	LEARNING OBJECTIVE	POS/AO	NNS	CONTENT	PAGE
Football strips	To identify simple relationships between variables. To make predictions based on simple relationships. To solve a problem in a logical, methodical way.	U & A 4b search for pattern in their results. U & A 4c make general statements. N 3a explore number sequences, explaining patterns and using simple relationships; progress to generalising. *Patterns and sequences, level C*	Solve mathematical problems, recognise and explain patterns and relationships, generalise and predict (Y4/5/6 p78–79).	Pupils investigate the number of different football strips which can be made when certain colours of shirts and shorts are available. Individual investigative activity.	54
Football leagues	To identify simple relationships between variables. To make predictions based on simple relationships. To solve a problem in a logical, methodical way.	U & A 4b search for pattern in their results. U & A 4c make general statements. N 3a explore number sequences, explaining patterns and using simple relationships; progress to generalising. *Functions and equations, level D*	Solve mathematical problems, recognise and explain patterns and relationships and predict (Y4/5/6 p78–79).	Pupils investigate the relationship between the number of teams in a league and the total number of matches which will be played during the season. Individual investigative activity.	58
Input-output machines	To accurately follow a set of rules involving various arithmetic operations. To use inputs and outputs to identify the rule which is being applied. To start to understand and use inverse operations.	N 3a use simple mappings. N 3f understand and use the relationships between the four operations, including inverses. *As above*	Recognise and explain patterns and relationships (Y4/5/6 p78–79). Use all four operations to solve word problems involving numbers in 'real life' (Y4/5/6 p82–83).	Several activities to introduce pupils to the idea of an input-output machine in which a rule is applied consistently to various inputs to produce an output each time. Various whole class and pairs activities.	59
Snakes and ladders, page 57; Find the rule, page 73; Hidden number, page 78					
Pentominoes on a 100-square	To add whole numbers up to 100 without a calculator. To use the number patterns in a 100-square to solve problems.	N 3d develop a variety of mental methods of computation with whole numbers up to 100. *Addition, level D*	Add several numbers (Y4/5/6 p42–43). Solve mathematical problems (Y4/5/6 p78–79).	Pupils place a pentomino on a 100-square and work out the sum of the five numbers it is covering. The aim is to find a pentomino with a particular total. Individual investigative activity.	62
House numbers, page 74					
The wall	To add one and two-digit numbers without a calculator. To identify relationships and make general statements.	U & A 4b search for pattern in their results. U & A 4c make general statements. N 3d develop a variety of mental methods of computation with whole numbers up to 100. *Addition, level C*	Add a pair of numbers mentally (Y3 p36–41; Y4/5/6 p44–47). Solve mathematical problems, recognise and predict (Y3 p62–63; Y4/5/6 p78–79).	The numbers in the bricks of a wall are combined in a particular way to produce an answer in the top brick. Pupils must investigate what happens to the top number when they change the numbers at the bottom. Individual investigative activity.	65
Add and subtract race, page 34; Addition squares, page 35; Cross numbers, page 37					

NUMBER KEY STAGE TWO

<table>
<tr><td rowspan="15">CALCULATIONS</td><td>ACTIVITY TITLE</td><td>LEARNING OBJECTIVE</td><td>POS/AO</td><td>NNS</td><td>CONTENT</td><td>PAGE</td></tr>
<tr><td>Multiplication squares</td><td>To know and use multiplication facts up to 10 by 10.</td><td>N 3c know the multiplication facts to 10x10.
Multiply, level C</td><td>Know multiplication facts (Y3 p52–53; Y4/5/6 p58–59).Solve mathematical problems (Y3 p52–53; Y4/5/6 p78–79.</td><td>Pupils reinforce their knowledge of multiplication facts by completing various multiplication grids. Individual worksheet-based activity.</td><td>68</td></tr>
<tr><td colspan="5">Multiplication square, page 38; Multiplication grids, page 98</td></tr>
<tr><td>The cardioid</td><td>To practise mental doubling strategies involving numbers up to 100. To use a pencil and ruler to draw straight lines.</td><td>N 3d develop a variety of mental methods of computation with whole numbers up to 100.
Multiply, level B</td><td>Know by heart or derive rapidly doubles (Y4/5/6 p58–59).</td><td>A visual pattern is produced when the numbers on a special clock face are joined to their doubles. Individual photocopiable sheet-based activity.</td><td>70</td></tr>
<tr><td>Maximize the product</td><td>To multiply two or more numbers without a calculator. To use findings to make predictions and generalisations.</td><td>U & A 4b search for pattern in their results.
U & A 4c make general statements.
N 3d develop a variety of mental methods of computation with whole numbers up to 100.
Multiply, level C</td><td>Use known number facts and place value to multiply mentally (Y4/5/6 p64–65). Solve mathematical problems, recognise and explain patterns and relationships, generalise and predict (Y4/5/6 p78–79).</td><td>Pupils must find the maximum product when a strip of mulitlink is broken into parts and the numbers in each part are multiplied together. Individual investigative activity.</td><td>72</td></tr>
<tr><td>Estimating decimal multipliers</td><td>To develop an understanding of place value in the context of decimals. To use trial and improvement methods. To appreciate that multiplication does not always make numbers bigger.</td><td>N 2b extend their understanding of the number system to decimals.
N 4c estimate and approximate solutions to problems.
Multiply, level D</td><td>Use decimal notation and know what each digit in a decimal fraction represents (Y4/5/6 p28–29). Understand the operation of multiplication (Y4/5/6 p52–53). Use known number facts and place value to multiply mentally (Y4/5/6 p64–65).</td><td>Number track game in which pupils must estimate the multiplier which will take them from their current space to the next. Game played in pairs.</td><td>74</td></tr>
<tr><td colspan="5">Missing number, page 71</td></tr>
<tr><td>Number centipedes</td><td>To halve even numbers without a calculator.</td><td>N 3d develop a variety of mental methods of computation with whole numbers up to 100.
Divide, level B</td><td>Derive doubles and halves quickly (Y3 p52–53; Y4/5/6 p58–59). Solve mathematical problems (Y3 p62–63; Y4/5/6 p78–79).</td><td>Pupils use a rule to generate number sequences and investigate how to make the longest sequence. Individual investigative activity.</td><td>77</td></tr>
<tr><td>Double or halve bingo</td><td>To practise mental doubling and halving strategies involving numbers up to 12.</td><td>N 3d develop a variety of mental methods of computation with whole numbers up to 100.
Multiply and divide, level B</td><td>Derive doubles and halves quickly (Y3 p52–53; Y4/5/6 p58–59). Solve mathematical problems (Y3 p62–63; Y4/5/6 p78–79).</td><td>The teacher rolls a dice and the pupils can cross off either double or half of the score. In later games pupils design their own bingo card with numbers of their own choice. Whole-class teacher-led game.</td><td>78</td></tr>
<tr><td colspan="5">Double the quantity, page 67</td></tr>
</table>

	ACTIVITY TITLE	LEARNING OBJECTIVE	POS/AO	NNS	CONTENT	PAGE
CHAPTER TITLE	Remainders	To divide two-digit numbers by single-digit numbers involving remainders.	N 3d develop a variety of mental methods of computation with whole numbers up to 100. *Divide, level C*	Understand the operation of division and the associated vocabulary (Y3 p48–49; Y4/5/6 p54–55). Understand the idea of a remainder (Y3 p50–51; Y4/5/6 p56 57).	Number track game in which pupils divide two numbers and work out the answer including any remainder. Dice game played in pairs.	80
	From 1 to 100	To practise mental skills involving all four operations. To use brackets correctly in arithmetical expressions.	N 3d develop a variety of mental methods of computation with whole numbers up to 100. *Add, subtract, multiply, divide, level D*	Add or subtract numbers mentally (Y4/5/6 p44–47). Multiply or divide numbers mentally (Y4/5/6 p64–65). Use brackets (Y4/5/6 p52–53).	Pupils combine four digits in various ways in an attempt to produce answers from 1 to 100. Individual open-ended activity.	82
	Three in a row	To practise mental skills involving a variety of arithmetical operations in the context of a strategy game.	N 3d develop a variety of mental methods of computation with whole numbers up to 100. *As above*	Add or subtract numbers mentally (Y3 p36–41; Y4/5/6 p44–47). Multiply or divide numbers mentally (Y3 p56–57; Y4/5/6 p64–65).	Game in which pupils roll two dice and combine the scores using any operation to produce an answer. The answer is covered on a number grid. Game played in pairs.	84
	Three dice bingo	To practise mental skills involving a variety of arithmetical operations.	N 3d develop a variety of mental methods of computation with whole numbers up to 100. *As above*	Add or subtract numbers mentally (Y3 p36–41; Y4/5/6 p44–47). Multiply or divide numbers mentally (Y3 p56–57; Y4/5/6 p64–65).	Pupils roll three dice and then have a set amount of time to make up to five different answers from the scores. Dice game played in small groups.	85
	Find…	To practise mental skills involving a variety of arithmetical operations.	N 3d develop a variety of mental methods of computation with whole numbers up to 100. *Add, subtract, level D*	Add or subtract numbers mentally (Y4/5/6 p44–47). Multiply numbers mentally (4/5/6 p64–65). Solve mathematical problems (Y4/5/6 p78–79).	Using a number grid pupils must find two or three numbers in a line which satisfy certain conditions eg find two numbers with a product of 24. Individual photocopiable sheet-based open-ended activity.	87
	Times and dates	To practise mental skills involving a variety of arithmetical operations. To use and apply knowledge of time and date notation.	N 3d develop a variety of mental methods of computation with whole numbers up to 100. *Time, level C*	Add or subtract numbers mentally (Y4/5/6 p44–47). Multiply or divide numbers mentally (Y4/5/6 p64–65). Use all four operations to solve problems involving time (Y4/5/6 p88–89).	Pupils solve various problems based on the numerical properties of times and dates. Individual photocopiable sheet-based activity.	91

Number Structure

At Key Stage One, pupils spend a large amount of time developing an understanding of the number system and place value. The aim is for children to develop confidence and a 'feel for number' before moving on to look at methods of calculation. This early work needs to be reinforced and extended during Key Stage Two in order to support children as they start to calculate using fractions, decimals and percentages.

Children need to build on their early understanding of halves and quarters, they need to understand number structure and place value associated with decimals and they need to be able to round decimal answers, particularly when using a calculator. All of these areas are considered in this chapter.

The first activity reinforces place value for whole numbers while the next considers place value in the context of multiplying and dividing by 10, 100 and 1000. This is followed by three activities that reinforce and extend early fractions work. The final activity provides valuable rounding practice.

PLACE VALUE DICE GAMES

To understand that the position of a digit affects its value. To practise mental addition skills involving two-digit numbers.

†† *Whole-class introduction followed by work in pairs and a whole-class plenary.*

⏱ *Introduction 10–15 minutes; main activity 10–15 minutes; plenary 10–15 minutes; total 30–45 minutes.*

Previous skills/knowledge needed
It is assumed that children will have a basic understanding of place value involving numbers up to 100.

Key background information
Children should have developed an understanding of place value during Key Stage One. However, throughout Key Stage Two opportunities should still be provided to reinforce this important concept because it is possible that many children will have failed to understand it the first time around, and those who do grasp it will need to be able to apply it in a wide range of contexts.

This activity comprises a selection of place value dice games that can be played either as a whole class or in pairs. The games are structured to form a complete lesson, although it is possible to use any one of the games individually to fill a spare five minutes at the end of a teaching session.

Preparation
Make copies of photocopiable page 93 so that there is one copy per child. Each pair of pupils will also need a ten-sided dice with faces numbered 0–9. An alternative to rolling the dice is to pick a card from a set numbered 0–9. Photocopiable page 94 can be used to produce these sets. Finally, draw the arrangement of boxes and symbols below on the board, large enough for all the children to see when sitting at their tables.

Resources
Photocopiable page 93, photocopiable page 94 (optional), a ten-sided dice (or sets of 0–9 number cards), pencils, board/flip chart.

What to do
Introduction
Ask the children to provide you with an example of a two-digit number and then write it in the two left-hand boxes, one digit per box. Next, point at the < symbol. Ask if anyone has seen this symbol before and if anyone knows what it means. Hopefully, one of the children will be able to tell you that it means 'is less than', otherwise explain that this is what it means. Write the words 'is less than' below the symbol. Ask the children to provide another two-digit number for the right-hand boxes so that the mathematical statement is correct. Write the number in the boxes, one digit per box, and reiterate the meaning of the < symbol. If necessary, rub out the two numbers and ask the children to provide further examples that make correct statements.

Tell the children that they are going to play a whole-class game. Each child will be using the same arrangement of boxes drawn on the board, including the < symbol. Explain that you will roll a ten-sided dice four times. After each roll they must write the digit in any one of their four boxes. The aim is to have written a correct statement after four rolls of the dice. Give each child a copy of photocopiable page 93 and point out which row of boxes must be used (the one labelled 'Game 1').

Roll a ten-sided dice (or ask a pupil to roll it), call out the score and then allow the children a few seconds to decide in which box to write the digit. Repeat this until you have rolled the dice four times. Ask the children to put up their hands if they have made a correct statement and tell them to put a 1 in the score box at the right-hand side of the photocopiable sheet. (Those children who have not written a correct statement should write in zero.) Invite children to come out and write their correct statements on the board. See how many different correct statements can be made using the four digits.

Repeat the game using the second row of boxes on the photocopiable sheet and again discuss the possible correct statements that can be made using the four digits.

Before playing game three, explain a new scoring system to the pupils. Tell them that if they write a correct statement they will score not just a single point but whatever the two-digit number is in the left-hand boxes. For example if a child has written 27 in the left-hand boxes, then he or she will score 27 points (as long as the complete statement is correct). Play game three and tell the children to record the number of points they have scored. Discuss the possible correct statements that can be made, perhaps by saying: *What is the maximum number of points you can score with these four digits?* Play game four in the same way as game three.

Main activity
For the main activity the children work in pairs and play a different dice game using rows 5–10 of the photocopiable sheet. Tell the children to take it in turns to roll the dice and write the digit in one of the boxes on their own photocopiable sheet. The dice is rolled eight times altogether, that is, four times each. At the end each child will have made two two-digit numbers. These must then be added together (the answer can be written on the photocopiable sheet to the right of the two numbers). The aim is to make a total that is as close as possible to 100. The player whose total is closest to 100 is the winner and scores 5 points.

When the children have completed games 5–10 they can play further games by drawing some more boxes on the reverse side of their photocopiable sheet.

Plenary
Draw this arrangement of boxes and symbols on the board.

Tell the children that you want to write three two-digit numbers in the boxes to make a correct statement. Then pose questions such as: *What can you tell me about the left and the middle numbers? What can you tell me about the middle and right numbers? How will the numbers be arranged as we move from left to right?* By asking these sorts of questions you should be able to elicit from the children the fact that the left-hand number is less than the middle number and the middle number is less than the right number. The three numbers will be in ascending order from left to right. Demonstrate this by writing in three numbers that make a correct statement.

Play the final game using row 11 of the photocopiable sheet. Explain to the children that you will roll a ten-sided dice six times. After each roll they must write the digit in one of their boxes, and the aim, as previously, is to make a correct statement. When you have completed the game, ask the children to provide examples of completely correct statements which they have made. A completely correct

statement (one that has three numbers in ascending order from left to right) scores 3 points. If anyone has made a partially correct statement (left is less than middle or middle is less than right but not both) then they can score 1 point. Play the game three more times using rows 12 to 14 of the photocopiable sheet.

Suggestion(s) for extension

Alternative scoring systems involving more complex calculations can be used during the main activity. The winner could score points according to how much closer he or she is to 100 than the loser. For example, if player one's total is 87 (13 away from 100) and player two's total is 106 (6 away from 100) then player two is the winner and scores 7 points (the difference between 13 and 6).

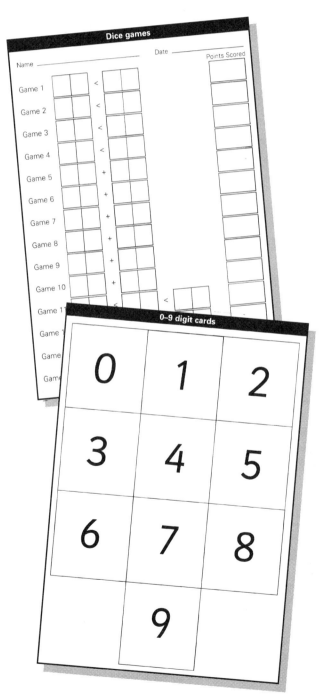

The games themselves can also be adapted to make them more demanding. For example they could involve the addition of three-digit numbers:

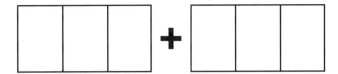

or involve both addition and subtraction:

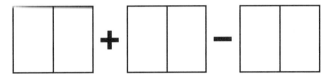

In both cases, appropriate target numbers will need to be identified beforehand, for example in the case of two three-digit numbers the target could be 500 or 1000.

Suggestion(s) for support

If the addition game is too demanding for some children then replace the + symbols on the photocopiable sheet with < symbols. Children could also play in pairs, roll the dice four times (twice each) and try to make a correct statement in the same way as in the introductory game.

Assessment opportunities

Observe the children carefully during the main activity and ask them to justify writing a digit in a particular box. Their responses will indicate their understanding of place value. Also ask pupils to explain how they added the two numbers mentally.

Reference to photocopiable sheets

Photocopiable page 93 provides a number of two-digit boxes that the children attempt to fill in correctly during various number games. It can be adapted in many ways to suit your own particular circumstances. You could produce three separate sheets, each focusing on only one of the three games, or you may like to produce a sheet that uses three-digit numbers, or one that involves addition and subtraction. Some of these possibilities are described in 'Suggestion(s) for extension' above.

Photocopiable page 94 provides a set of 0–9 number cards which you can photocopy for children to use during the activity if you do not have ten-sided dice.

TENS, HUNDREDS AND THOUSANDS

To be able to multiply and divide by 10, 100, 1000, and so on.

†† *Whole-class introduction followed by work in pairs and a whole-class plenary.*

🕐 *Introduction 5–10 minutes; main activity 15–20 minutes; plenary 10–15 minutes; total 30–45 minutes.*

Previous skills/knowledge needed

This activity assumes that children are already aware of the effects of multiplying and dividing by 10, 100, 1000, and so on.

Key background information

The ability to multiply and divide by 10, 100 and 1000 is an important mental skill which children need to be able to carry out quickly. The number patterns which result from these operations can initially be explored with the aid of a calculator but once children are aware of the patterns they need to spend time reinforcing and applying them by doing activities such as this one. Always explain these operations in terms of the digits moving left or right into another column, for example when multiplying 3 by 100 the 3 moves from the units column to the hundreds column and the resulting gaps are filled with two zeros. This approach reinforces the concept of place value and is preferable to common alternatives such as 'Move the decimal point two places' and 'Stick a couple of zeros on the end'.

Preparation

Make copies of photocopiable page 95 so that there is one copy for each pair of pupils. (If you are going to be reusing the sheets you may wish to make them more durable by photocopying them onto card and/or laminating them.) Each pair will also require an ordinary six-sided dice and a six-sided dice with faces labelled '×10', '×100', '×1000', '÷10', '÷100' and '÷1000'. These can be produced from blank dice which are available from educational suppliers or alternatively you could blank out the faces of ordinary six-sided dice. You may also want to prepare some number problems written on pieces of card (see the introduction opposite).

Resources

Six-sided dice, adapted six-sided dice as described in 'Preparation', counters in two colours (you will need three colours if you have a group of three), calculators, photocopiable page 95, pencils, paper, board/flip chart.

What to do

Introduction

Recap previous work you have carried out on the theme of multiplying and dividing by 10, 100 and 1000. One way to do this is to hold up pieces of card with problems written on them, for example '7 × 10' and '13 × 100', and ask individual children to give you the answer. Use a wide selection of questions and match these to the abilities of the children you ask. Work through one or two of the answers on the board to remind the class of the general principles involved when multiplying and dividing by 10, 100 and 1000. For example, 13 × 100 could be explained in terms of each digit moving two columns to the left like this:

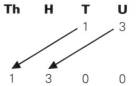

Main activity

Organize the children into pairs, although if there are an odd number in the class it is possible for children to play as a group of three. Give each pair a copy of photocopiable page 95, some counters, the two dice, a calculator, pencils and paper. Explain that each child must take turns to roll the two dice. He or she should then call out the answer to the multiplication or division, find the answer on the grid and cover it with a counter of his or her own colour. Any disputes can be resolved using the calculator. The aim is for each child to get three of his or her own counters next to each other in a line in any direction. Children should record on paper each calculation they make, including the answer. This will allow you to check the children's calculations.

If you feel that children have played the game for long enough but there is still some time remaining you could ask them to list in order of size all of the possible answers that can be made by rolling the two dice. Remove the

photocopiable sheet from the children during this part of the activity to prevent them from simply listing the numbers that appear on it.

Plenary

Ask the children to provide you with all of the possible answers, in order of size, which can be made by rolling the two dice in the main activity. Pupils could come out one at a time and record the numbers on the board. Try to ensure that all the children contribute to this discussion, not just those who have already worked out the answers as part of the main activity.

Further discussions could focus on questions such as: *What is 4 × 300?* This is the next logical stage since it follows on from the work in the main activity. You could also ask the children to explain how they would tackle these sorts of questions and discuss suitable strategies. Most are likely to be based on the fact that:

$$4 \times 300 = 4 \times 3 \times 100$$

Since the order in which we multiply three numbers does not affect the answer (multiplication is associative), the question becomes 12 × 100, which can be tackled in the same way as the main activity.

Suggestion(s) for extension

Children requiring extension work could use alternatives to the ordinary six-sided dice, for example a twelve or twenty-sided dice. You would need to amend photocopiable page 95 so that it contains answers appropriate to the dice being used.

Suggestion(s) for support

It might be appropriate for some children to focus only on multiplication. These children could use a special six-sided dice with faces labelled '×10', '×100' and '×1000' (each label would appear on two faces). Again, photocopiable page 95 would need to be amended so that it contains appropriate answers (10, 100, 1000, 20, 200, 2000, …, 60, 600 and 6000).

Assessment opportunities

Make a mental note of the children's responses during the introduction and also observe their progress during the main activity, particularly the speed at which they are able to work out the correct answer. This, together with their written work will provide an insight into their ability to multiply and divide by 10, 100 and 1000.

Opportunities for IT

The computer program *Tenners*, produced by MicroSMILE, could be used to demonstrate and reinforce some of the key points in this activity. Several numbers that use the same digits are displayed on the screen, for example 3.5,

0.035 and 350, and pupils must multiply or divide the numbers by 10, 100 or 1000 to make them all the same. The program is available for BBC, RM Nimbus PC-186 and Archimedes computers.

Display ideas

You could produce a display that reinforces the basic principles and patterns associated with multiplying and dividing by 10, 100 and 1000. This would provide the children with a constant reminder so that these eventually become memorized facts which they can recall instantly.

Reference to photocopiable sheet

Photocopiable page 95 displays a honeycomb of various numbers. The children must attempt to cover the numbers by rolling two dice, calling out the associated multiplication or division answer and then covering the answers on the photocopiable sheet. Some of the numbers on the sheet will need to be altered if alternative dice are used as described in the 'Suggestion(s) for extension and support' sections.

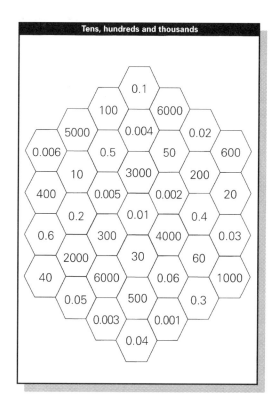

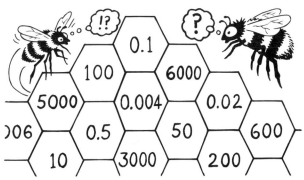

FRACTIONS WITH PATTERN BLOCKS

To demonstrate an understanding of fractions through shape-filling activities.

†† *Whole-class introduction followed by individual work and a whole-class plenary.*

🕐 *Introduction 10–15 minutes; main activity 20–25 minutes; plenary 15–20 minutes; total 45–60 minutes.*

Previous skills/knowledge needed

Children should be familiar with the concept of a fraction and have begun to consider fractions other than simply halves and quarters.

Key background information

At Key Stage One, children are provided with a basic introduction to simple fractions such as halves and quarters. This activity builds on this early work by first reinforcing it and then extending it to look at fractions such as thirds, sixths and eighths. A practical, 'hands-on' approach is adopted using Pattern blocks so that pupils can continue to develop their understanding of fractions in visual as well as numerical terms.

Preparation

Make copies of photocopiable pages 96, 97, 98 and 99 so that there is one copy of each sheet for every child. Children may need two copies of photocopiable page 99 and additional copies of pages 96, 97 and 98 for the extension activities. On the board or on separate pieces of card draw several shapes, for example circles, squares and rectangles (you can draw more than one of each shape). Draw lines to divide one or two of the shapes into halves, some of the shapes into thirds, some into quarters, some into fifths, and so on. Ensure that in every case the original shape has been divided into equal parts. Then shade in part of each shape to represent a different fraction,

for example shade in one-half, one-quarter, one-third, one-eighth, three-quarters, two-thirds, two-fifths, and so on. These are required during the introduction.

Resources

Tubs of Pattern blocks (two or three tubs should be enough for a class of 30 pupils), photocopiable pages 96–99, coloured pencils or crayons corresponding to the colours of the Pattern blocks, some shapes (as described in 'Preparation').

What to do

Introduction

Recap earlier work on fractions by pointing to or holding up one of the shaded shapes you have drawn (start with half) and asking the children what fraction of the shape is shaded. Then ask them how they know that it is half and what half actually means. The key point to stress is that the shape has been divided into two equal parts and one of them is shaded. Repeat this with the other shapes, again stressing that the shape is always divided into equal parts. (You may also like to recap or introduce formal fractions notation.) Start by asking the children how we write one-half using symbols and then ask them what the top (numerator) and bottom (denominator) numbers mean. These can be explained in terms of how many equal parts the shape has been divided into and how many of them have been shaded.

Main activity

Give each child a copy of photocopiable pages 96 and 97 and ask them to follow the instructions. Explain that they must first fill each shape on photocopiable page 97 with Pattern block pieces according to the specifications on page 96. Stress to the children that they must always use exactly two colours each time (two different types of Pattern block pieces). When they have done that they should then shade in the shape in the corresponding

colours. Once they have completed photocopiable page 97 give them copies of pages 98 and 99 to complete.

Plenary

Start by asking the children if there were any Pattern block pieces that were not used during the main activity (the orange square and the brown rhombus are not used).

Next, go through the solutions to each problem on the photocopiable sheets. Ask the children to hold up their shaded shapes and describe which pieces they used to fill them. Always ask the children to explain how they know that the shape is, for example, one third green and two-thirds blue. This is often best explained in terms of green triangle equivalents. For example, when filling the star shape, start by asking pupils how many green triangles can be fitted into it (the answer is twelve so stress that the star can be divided into twelve equal parts). Then ask how many green triangles are in the pupil's shaded star (it should be four) and therefore what fraction of the star is green.

Finally ask the children how many green triangles the four blue rhombuses are equivalent to (the answer is eight) and therefore what fraction of the star is shaded blue. The same approach can be adopted to explain all of the shadings, including the one which is impossible. The concept of equivalent fractions can also be reinforced during the discussions.

Suggestion(s) for extension

Those children who successfully complete the photocopiable sheets can go back to some of the instructions and see whether they can be completed in more than one way, for instance using different colour combinations. Hand out fresh copies of the photocopiable sheets for the children to record their new solutions. As a further challenge you could also impose additional constraints, for example the children could be told to shade their shapes so that they have a line of symmetry.

Suggestion(s) for support

The main activity should be accessible to all the children since the early questions are fairly easy. You might want to ask some pupils to attempt initially only those questions which are appropriate to their ability, for example those involving halves and quarters. The more demanding questions could be attempted later, perhaps with the assistance of an adult.

Assessment opportunities

During the main activity observe pupils carefully and ask them to explain how they know that the shape is, for example, one-third green and two-thirds yellow or how they know that it is not possible to fill half of the triangle. Their responses will provide an insight into their understanding of fractions.

Display ideas

The completed photocopiable sheets can be used to produce a colourful display.

Reference to photocopiable sheets

Photocopiable pages 97–99 provide a variety of shapes. Using the instructions on photocopiable page 96 the children must attempt to fill the shapes with varying amounts of Pattern block pieces.

The tables on the next page indicate how the questions on the photocopiable sheets can be solved.

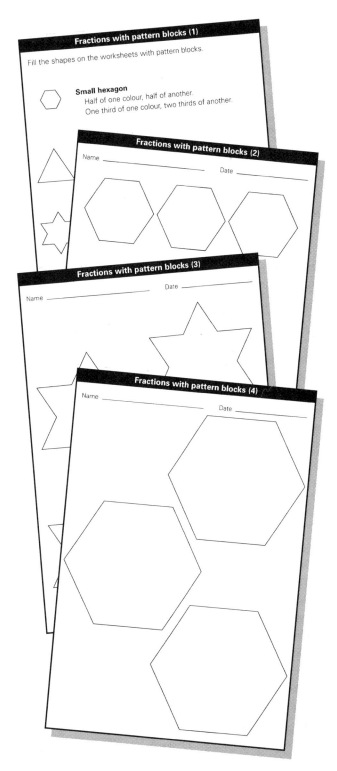

Small Hexagon

half	half
1 red trapezium	3 green triangles

one-third	two-thirds
1 blue rhombus	4 green triangles
2 green triangles	2 blue rhombuses

Triangle

It is impossible to fill the triangle with half of one colour and half of another.

one-third	two-thirds
1 red trapezium	6 green triangles
3 green triangles	1 yellow hexagon
3 green triangles	2 red trapeziums
3 green triangles	3 blue rhombuses

Star

half	half
1 yellow hexagon	6 green triangles
2 red trapeziums	6 green triangles
3 blue rhombuses	6 green triangles

one-quarter	three-quarters
1 red trapezium	9 green triangles
3 green triangles	3 red trapeziums

one-third	two-thirds
2 blue rhombuses	8 green triangles
4 green triangles	4 blue rhombuses

one-sixth	five-sixths
1 blue rhombus	10 green triangles
2 green triangles	5 blue rhombuses

Large Hexagon

half	half
2 yellow hexagons	12 green triangles
2 yellow hexagons	6 blue rhombuses
4 red trapeziums	12 green triangles
4 red trapeziums	6 blue rhombuses
6 blue rhombuses	12 green triangles

one-quarter	three-quarters
1 yellow hexagon	6 red trapeziums
1 yellow hexagon	9 blue rhombuses
1 yellow hexagon	18 green triangles
2 red trapeziums	9 blue rhombuses
2 red trapeziums	18 green triangles
3 blue rhombuses	6 red trapeziums
3 blue rhombuses	18 green triangles
3 blue rhombuses	3 yellow hexagons
6 green triangles	3 yellow hexagons
6 green triangles	6 red trapeziums
6 green triangles	9 blue rhombuses

one-third	two-thirds
4 blue rhombuses	16 green triangles
8 green triangles	8 blue rhombuses

one-sixth	five-sixths
2 blue rhombuses	20 green triangles
4 green triangles	10 blue rhombuses

one-eighth	seven-eighths
1 red trapezium	21 green triangles
3 green triangles	7 red trapeziums

three-eighths	five-eighths
3 red trapeziums	15 green triangles
9 green triangles	5 red trapeziums

CONGRUENT HALVES

To apply knowledge of simple fractions. To
understand the concept of congruence.

†† *Whole-class introduction followed by individual*
work and a whole-class plenary.

🕐 *Introduction 10–15 minutes; main activity 20–25*
minutes; plenary 15–20 minutes; total 45–60
minutes.

Previous skills/knowledge needed

Children should be familiar with simple fractions such as
halves, thirds and quarters.

Key background information

The key point that needs to be made when teaching
fractions is that the whole is divided into equal parts. For
example, when cutting a sheet of paper in half the two
resulting pieces must have the same area. Often we try
to reinforce this point by making the pieces identical, that
is, one piece can be fitted exactly on top of the other. We
say that the two shapes are *congruent*. Two shapes are
congruent if they are exactly the same size and the same
shape. The simplest way to check for congruence is to
place one shape on top of the other. If they coincide exactly
when they are superimposed then they are congruent. It
does not matter if one of the shapes has to be flipped
over to make them fit; they are still congruent. An
alternative is to make a tracing of one shape and fit this
over the other. Again, it does not matter if the tracing paper
has to be turned over to make the outline fit the other
shape. This investigative activity reinforces earlier work
on fractions and also introduces children to the important
concept of congruence.

Preparation

Make four large squares, say 40cm × 40cm, out of paper
or card. Leave two of the squares blank but divide the
other two in half as shown below.

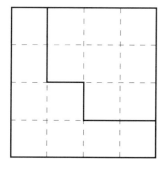

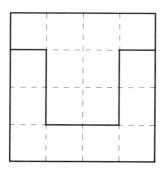

The easiest way to do this is to draw a 4 × 4 grid in pencil
on each square and then draw the dividing lines using a
thicker marker pen. Do not rub out the grid lines; you might
need to refer to these during your explanations and
discusions. Also make copies of photocopiable pages 100,
101 and 102.

Resources

Shapes made from paper or card as described in
'Preparation', photocopiable pages 100, 101 and 102,
rulers, pencils, scissors (optional).

What to do

Introduction

Hold up one of the blank squares you prepared earlier and
say to the children: *How could I quickly divide this square*
in half? The responses will probably include drawing or
folding along the diagonal or along a vertical or horizontal
line. Use a ruler and marker pen to divide the square as
suggested by one of the children. Ensure that the
suggestion you follow results in two congruent halves.
Hold up the other blank square and divide it in half a
different way as suggested by one of the children, again
ensuring that it results in two congruent halves. Attach
both squares to the wall so that everyone can see them.
Then hold up one of the other squares you prepared earlier
and say: *Has this square been divided in half?* Follow this
with questions such as: *How do you know that it has been*
divided in half? Repeat this with the final square, again
asking the children to explain their answers. By making
use of the 16 smaller squares drawn in pencil you should
be able to convince everyone that both of the large squares
have been divided in half, that is, each half comprises eight
small squares.

Then hold up the two squares and say: *Look closely at*
the way these two squares have been divided in half. Why
are they different to the two I drew a few minutes ago?
(Point at the two squares attached to the wall.) Provide
additional prompts if necessary, for example, *What do you*
notice about the shape of these two halves (pointing)
compared with these two halves (pointing)?

Introduce the word 'congruent', explaining that two
shapes are congruent if they are identical, enabling one to
be fitted exactly on top of the other. Demonstrate this by
cutting each of the squares in half with a pair of scissors
and attempting to fit one half on top of the other. Finally,
stress that all four squares have been cut in half (reiterate
the earlier discussion by asking the children to explain why)
but two of them have been cut into congruent halves and
the other two have been cut into halves that are not
congruent.

Main activity

Give each child a copy of photocopiable pages 100, 101

and 102. Explain to the children that they must follow the instructions on photocopiable page 100. Stress that they must divide the shapes only by drawing, not by cutting them up.

Observe the children carefully as they are working and pick up on any errors or misconceptions. In some instances, if a child has not divided a shape into congruent pieces, then it might be appropriate to ask him or her to cut out the pieces and try to fit each one on top of the other. This should help them to develop an understanding of the concept of congruence.

Provide appropriate prompts if necessary, for example, if a pupil is having difficulty dividing the L-shape into congruent quarters, encourage him or her to make use of the spots on the paper. Say to the child: *How many small squares can the L-shape be divided into?* (The answer is twelve.) Follow this with: *So how many squares will be in each quarter?* Finally, say: *So you need to divide the shape into four pieces, each one made from three small squares.* Similarly, children can think of the shapes on the triangular spotted paper in terms of small equilateral triangles. This reinforces the idea of dividing a whole into equal parts and also the principle of equivalent fractions, in other words three-twelfths is the same as one-quarter.

Plenary
Use the plenary session to work through the solutions to each problem. Ask individual children to hold up their drawings for the rest of the class to see. In some cases it might be appropriate to cut the shape up to demonstrate that the pieces are in fact congruent. Also, be aware that there is often more than one solution to each problem and so some or all of the possibilities could be discussed.

You could also ask children to explain how they know that the shape has been divided in half, or into thirds or quarters, without actually cutting out the pieces and fitting them on top of one another to check. The explanations could be based on counting the small squares or triangles in each piece and would thus reinforce the idea of equivalent fractions.

Suggestion(s) for extension
When the children have worked out a solution to each problem, ask them to go back and find a second solution to each one (many of the problems can be answered in more than one way). You could also ask them to draw a new shape, not already on the photocopiable sheet, that can be divided into congruent halves, quarters and thirds.

Suggestion(s) for support
The activity should be accessible to all children although it might be appropriate for some to focus just on halves and perhaps quarters. Ask the children to find more than one solution to some of the easier instructions, for example halving or quartering a square.

Congruent Halves

Congruent Thirds

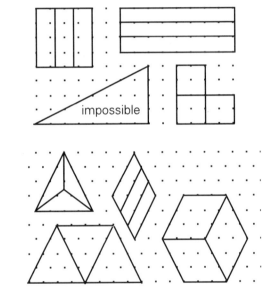

Congruent Quarters

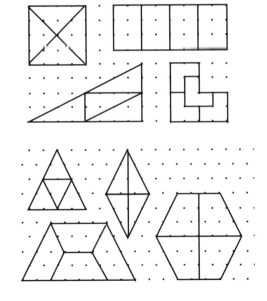

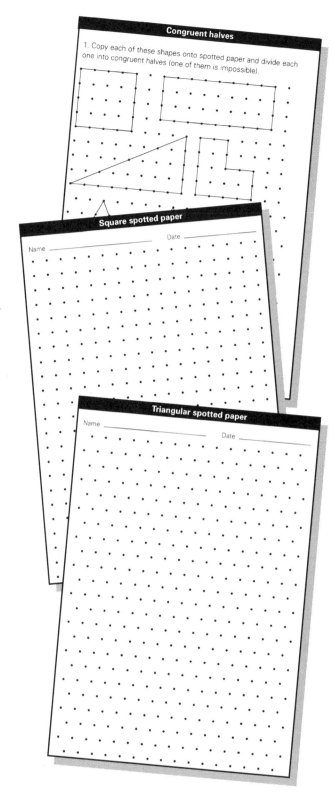

Assessment opportunities

Your observations and discussions with the children during the main activity will provide an insight into their understanding of congruence and simple fractions.

Display ideas

The visual nature of the children's completed photocopiable sheets means that they can be used to produce a valuable display reinforcing the work on both fractions and congruence.

Reference to photocopiable sheets

Photocopiable page 100 poses a number of problems about congruence which the children have to attempt to solve. Photocopiable pages 101 and 102 provide square and triangular spotted paper on which the children should work out their solutions.

The diagrams on the opposite page show one solution to each question (unless it is impossible). In many cases there are several other possible solutions.

MULTILINK MAKE HALF

To understand the concept of 'half'. To apply this in a practical investigation.

†† *Whole-class introduction followed by work in groups and a whole-class plenary.*

🕐 *Introduction 10–15 minutes; main activity 25–30 minutes; plenary 10–15 minutes; total 45–60 minutes.*

Previous skills/knowledge needed

Children should be familiar with halves and have some experience of 3-D shapes.

Key background information

For most children the concept of 'half' is a fairly easy one to grasp. The next stage is to provide reinforcement of the basic concepts as well as opportunities for children to apply their knowledge and understanding in various investigative and problem-solving situations. This activity provides such an opportunity.

Preparation

Ensure that you have a supply of multilink cubes for children to use.

Resources

Multilink cubes, pencils, paper.

What to do

Introduction

The children will need to be sitting at their tables in groups during the introduction. Start by asking if anyone knows what a cuboid is. Let pupils explain and describe a cuboid in their own words to the rest of the class. Introduce terminology such as 'faces', 'edges' and 'corners' if you feel that it is appropriate for the age and ability of the pupils. The key points are that a cuboid has six faces that are all squares or rectangles.

Next, place a tray of multilink cubes on each table and ask everyone to quickly make a cuboid and then hold their cuboids in the air so that you and the other children can see them. Reiterate the features of a cuboid that were discussed earlier.

Main activity

Tell the children that they must make another cuboid. However, this time half of the multilink must be in one colour and half in another. Check the children's cuboids as they are making them, picking up on any errors or misunderstandings. When the children have finished, ask everyone to hold up their cuboid so that you can quickly see them all.

Next, tell the children that you want them to do the same again but this time, in addition, each face of the cuboid must show half of one colour and half of the other. Some pupils may already have a cuboid that has one or more faces showing half-and-half. Hold these up as examples for everyone to see and also show examples of faces that are not half-and-half. Stress to the pupils that they must make a cuboid that is half-and-half on all six faces. After a few minutes stop the class and hold up one or two examples of cuboids that satisfy the conditions and also one or two that do not.

For the next part of the activity the pupils should collaborate in small groups. Explain that they must look at the different cuboids that have been correctly made according to the instructions given and investigate for which numbers of multilink this is possible. Ask the children to record their findings, perhaps by writing down the dimensions of the cuboids that satisfy the conditions and the numbers of multilink used. Another possibility is for the children to draw the cuboids.

All of the cuboids that satisfy the conditions are made from numbers of multilink that are multiples of four. Hopefully, many of the pupils will be able to spot this for themselves.

Plenary

Use this time to discuss the outcomes of the investigation and the conclusions reached. Ask the children to hold up cuboids that have been made correctly. Record the number of multilink on the board and invite pupils to explain the pattern. When the children think they have spotted the pattern and correctly say that the number of multilink is always a multiple of four, challenge them by asking questions such as: *Are you sure you cannot do it with ten multilink? How do you know it is not possible? What would a ten multilink cuboid look like? Why could it not be half-and-half on every face?*

If some pupils have been using multilink prisms to carry out the extension activity described below, then these outcomes and conclusions can also be discussed.

Suggestion(s) for extension

If you have a supply of multilink prisms (you will need the right-angled prisms – two prisms can be connected to form a cube) then the children could investigate whether using these affects the outcome of the investigation. For example, is it now possible to make a cuboid out of ten multilink that satisfies the conditions? (Note: two prisms count as one multilink cube.) The introduction of these prisms does in fact affect the outcome of the investigation. It is now possible to satisfy the conditions using numbers of multilink that are even numbers.

Suggestion(s) for support

Some pupils will need prompts to help them spot that all of the half-and-half cuboids are made from numbers of multilink that are multiples of four. The first stage is for them to make several cuboids that satisfy the conditions. You will need to check these carefully for errors and ask questions if necessary such as: *How much red can you see on this face? How much blue? Is it half-and-half?* The next stage is for them to be able to work out (or simply count) how many multilink are in each one. Finally, you might need to help them to spot the number pattern by saying, for example: *So there are four multilink in this one, eight in this one and twelve in this one. What do you notice about the numbers?*

Assessment opportunities

In the case of the less able children your observations will provide you with an insight into their understanding of the concept of half. Other pupils will fully understand halves and so you can focus on their ability to work in an investigative way, to spot patterns in the results and to make conclusions.

Display ideas

The multilink cuboids could be labelled appropriately and used to form a table-top display. If children have drawn their cuboids these could be mounted and displayed on the wall.

ROUND AND ROUND

To round decimals to the nearest whole number.
†† *Whole-class introduction followed by work in pairs or small groups and a whole-class plenary.*
🕐 *Introduction 10–15 minutes; main activity 25–30 minutes; plenary 10–15 minutes; total 45–60 minutes.*

Previous skills/knowledge needed

Children will need to be familiar with decimals, for example through reading decimal values on number lines or linear scales. They should also have some experience of rounding to the nearest ten or hundred.

Key background information

It is important that children get into the habit of checking their calculations by estimating roughly what the answer should be, especially when using a calculator. However, in order to estimate, children need to be able to approximate, that is, they first need to round the numbers used in the calculation, perhaps to the nearest hundred, the nearest ten or the nearest whole number. Pupils must therefore be given opportunities to practise their rounding skills. An essential teaching resource when doing work on approximation is a number line. This should be used as part of a 'common sense' approach to rounding, which should involve asking questions such as: *Is it nearer to 70 or 80?* Or *Is it nearer to 3 or 4?* This approach, used in conjunction with an appropriate number line, removes the need for children to learn the traditional rules associated with rounding. The only convention they need to be aware of is the one adopted when the number lies exactly halfway between the upper and lower bounds, that is, they must round up.

Preparation
Make copies of photocopiable page 103 so that there is one for each pair or small group. You may like to copy these onto card or laminate them in order to make them more durable. Each pair or group will also need a six-sided dice but with the 1 changed to a 7 (or simply tell the children to read the 1 as a 7). Attach a large number line to the wall, ranging from 0 to 3 with the whole numbers labelled and marks for the tenths clearly visible but not labelled.

Resources
A number line as described in 'Preparation', photocopiable page 103, six-sided dice, counters, paper, pencils, calculators.

What to do
Introduction
Recap earlier work on rounding by asking questions such as: *What is 239 to the nearest hundred?* and *What is 68 to the nearest ten?* Use further prompts to reinforce the approach, for example *Is it nearer to 200 or 300?* and *Is it nearer to 60 or 70?* Remind the children what they must

do if the number lies exactly halfway by including a question such as: *What is 450 to the nearest hundred?* By convention, numbers that lie halfway are always rounded up.

Move across to the large number line on the wall. Point to the location of a decimal number, for example 1.8, and ask the children what the number is. Repeat this with other numbers on the line. Also point at, or mark with a pen, a number that lies exactly halfway between the tenths, for example, 2.35, and ask pupils to tell you what it is. Explain and discuss these decimal numbers if necessary.

Write this arithmetic on the board.

$$17 \div 13$$

Give a calculator to one of the children and ask him or her to work out the answer and call it out. Write the answer on the board, just as it appears in the calculator display. Ask a different pupil to come out and point approximately to where the answer is on the number line. Mark the number on the line with a pen or use an arrow on a small piece of card. Then ask the children what the answer is to the nearest whole number. Help them by asking: *Is it nearer to 1 or 2?*

Repeat this with other divisions such as 29 ÷ 11 and 31 ÷ 12.

Main activity
Give each pair or small group a copy of photocopiable page 103 and a six-sided dice (with the 1 replaced by a 7), a calculator, pencils and paper. Tell each child to place a counter on one of the numbers on the track. Pupils should then take turns to roll the dice and move their counter in a clockwise direction according to the dice score. Then,

using a calculator, they must divide the number they land on by the score on the dice and write down the exact answer on their sheet of paper. Finally, they must write down the answer to the nearest whole number while the next player is having his or her turn. Play continues until everyone has had an agreed number of turns, for example ten or fifteen. The aim is simply to round the answers correctly.

While the children are playing the game, move around the groups and quickly check the pupils' rounded answers.

Plenary

Extend the work covered during the introduction to consider rounding to one decimal place. Start by recapping earlier decimals work on hundredths and use the large number line to assist your explanations. Use a pen to divide the number line between, for example 2.5 and 2.6, into ten equal parts. Point to the location of a decimal number, for example 2.53, and ask the children what the number is. Ask them to round the number to one decimal place and offer help by saying: *Is it nearer to 2.5 or 2.6?* Make use of the calculator answers produced earlier, for example $31 \div 12 = 2.583$, and ask the children to round the answer to one decimal place, again asking: *Is it nearer to 2.5 or 2.6?* You could also ask the children to call out some of the calculator answers generated during the main activity and round these to one decimal place.

Suggestion(s) for extension

If you feel that some children have had sufficient practice

at rounding to the nearest whole number, ask them to arrange all of the calculator answers on their sheet in order of size. Alternatively some pairs or groups of pupils could repeat the main activity but this time round the answers to one decimal place. It should be possible to explain this to able pupils very quickly.

Suggestion(s) for support

Less able children might benefit from adult assistance. A number line could be used to explain how to round the answers.

Assessment opportunities

Check pupils' rounded answers during the main activity and respond to any errors and misconceptions. Any answers that you do not check during the main activity can be marked later.

Display ideas

The large number line used during the introduction and plenary could become a permanent feature of the classroom and used to support future work on decimals.

Reference to photocopiable sheet

Photocopiable page 103 shows a variety of different numbers. Starting at any number, the children roll the dice and divide the number they land on by the dice score. The aim is for them to round the number correctly.

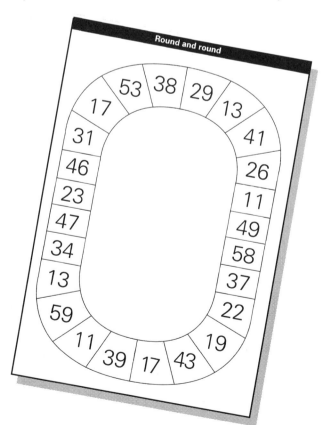

Round and round

53 38 29 13 17 31 41 46 26 23 11 47 49 34 58 13 37 59 22 11 39 17 43 19

Number Relationships

This aspect of mathematics is concerned with developing an awareness and understanding of the properties of numbers, their similarities and differences, and the relationships that exist between them. It therefore includes work on sets and sequences of special numbers and also a large amount of work on pattern since pattern lies at the heart of mathematics at all levels. At Key Stage One, children's experience of pattern is mainly in visual terms but at Key Stage Two this needs to be extended to look at the numerical patterns that underlie physical and spatial situations. The aim is for children to be able to spot patterns, to continue patterns, and to make predictions and general statements based on their findings. This is, in fact, early algebra work and it is of crucial importance if children are to be properly equipped to tackle problem-solving and investigative work at Key Stage Three.

The first five activities in this chapter focus on special numbers and provide a wide range of strategies for introducing and reinforcing this area of work. This is followed by eight activities which present various situations where there are underlying patterns and relationships for pupils to identify and explore. The final activity looks at input-output machines which is another key aspect of early algebra work. Many of the activities require pupils to carry out calculations of various sorts and so it could be argued that they belong in chapter three. However, despite involving calculations, the main focus of these activities is on special numbers, or on patterns and relationships, and so it is in this chapter where they belong.

MULTILINK PRIMES

To understand prime numbers and factors. To find prime numbers through a practical investigation involving multiplication.

†† *Whole-class introduction followed by individual work and a whole-class plenary.*

🕑 *Introduction 5–10 minutes; main activity 25–30 minutes; plenary 15–20 minutes; total 45–60 minutes.*

Previous skills/knowledge needed
It is assumed that children will be familiar with multiplication involving answers up to 100.

Key background information
Prime numbers are divisible only by themselves and 1, or put another way, they have only two factors. The first prime number is 2, followed by 3, 5 and 7. This activity introduces children to the idea of prime numbers, but not by simply stating the definition or a rule for finding them. Instead children use their existing knowledge and understanding to find prime numbers for themselves through practical investigation using multilink cubes.

Preparation
Make copies of photocopiable page 104 so that there is one for each child and ensure that there is a tray of multilink cubes for each table.

Resources
Photocopiable page 104, multilink cubes, pencils.

What to do
Introduction
During the introduction the children need to be sat at their tables with access to a tray of multilink cubes. Ask the children to quickly make a rectangle out of multilink, that is, a rectangular arrangement of cubes which is just one layer deep. Tell the children to hold up their rectangle when they have finished it. Pick up on any errors or misunderstandings and praise those children who quickly produced a rectangle. Use one of the children's rectangles as an example and ask questions such as: *How many cubes long is it? How many cubes wide?* and *How many cubes have been used altogether?* Ask the children to explain how they worked out the final answer. Repeat this using other children's rectangles as examples. If someone has made a square then use it as an example to discuss. If none of the children have made a square then point out that they could have made one since a square is a special

sort of rectangle. Recap the examples you have discussed by saying, for example: *So, this rectangle is made from 8 cubes, this one is made from 15 cubes, and this square is made from 16 cubes.* Finally say: *I wonder which other numbers of cubes can be arranged to make a rectangle?*

Main activity
Give each child a copy of photocopiable page 104. Tell the children that you want them to make some more rectangles out of multilink. Explain that they must count or work out how many cubes have been used and then cross off or shade that number on the 100-square on their photocopiable sheet. The aim is to find out which numbers of multilink up to 100 can be used to make a rectangle and which numbers cannot. Explain that for this activity a strip of multilink (say, 6 or 7 cubes in a line) does not count as a rectangle. Hold up an example to aid your explanation (a child may have made a strip during the introduction).

Plenary
Start by discussing which numbers have been crossed off the photocopiable sheet by working through the numbers from 1 to 100. For each number that has been crossed off, ask the children to tell you the dimensions of their rectangle. In many cases there will have been more than one way of making the rectangle and in some cases there are several possibilities. Try to identify all of the possibilities for each number that has been crossed off. At an appropriate point introduce the word 'factor' and explain it in terms of the possible dimensions of the rectangles made from a particular number of multilink. For example, with 24 multilink it is possible to make a 2×12, a 3×8 and a 4×6 rectangle. The factors of 24 are therefore

2, 12, 3, 8, 4 and 6. Explain that 1 and 24 are also factors because you can make a 1×24 rectangle (although for this activity children were not allowed to use widths of 1).

Continue to work through some or all of the numbers that have been crossed off, discussing the dimensions of the possible rectangles and therefore the factors of each number.

Finally, discuss those numbers that have not been crossed off. Quickly work through them and then introduce the children to the expression 'prime number'. Ask the children how many factors each of these prime numbers have got and use this as the basis of a possible definition, that is, prime numbers have only two factors, or in practical terms, prime numbers cannot be used to make rectangles apart from a rectangle which has a width of 1.

Suggestion(s) for extension
Some children might prefer to cross numbers off the 100-square without actually making the rectangles, relying instead on their multiplication skills. If children adopt this approach then it is important to ask them to explain their thinking by asking questions such as: *Why have you crossed off that number?* and *What would the dimensions of the rectangle be?*

Those children who complete the initial investigation could list all of the possible dimensions (factors) for each number they have crossed off. In this way they could investigate which number between 1 and 100 can be made in the most ways (in other words which number has the most factors).

Suggestion(s) for support
The nature of the activity is such that it should be accessible to all children and differentiation will be by outcome.

Assessment opportunities
During the main activity, point to particular numbers which children have crossed off and ask them what the dimensions of the rectangle would be. If there is a second possibility ask them to work out quickly what it is. This will provide an insight into the children's ability to use multiplication.

Display ideas
The children's shaded 100-squares can be displayed together with lists of factors for those numbers which have been shaded.

Reference to photocopiable sheet
Photocopiable page 104 provides a 1–100 number square. The children make rectangles out of multilink, work out the numbers of cubes used and then cross off that number in the square. At the end, the numbers that have not been crossed off will be the prime numbers.

Multilink primes

Name _____   Date _____

1	2	3	4	5	6	7	8	9	10
11	12	13	14	15	16	17	18	19	20
21	22	23	24	25	26	27	28	29	30
31	32	33	34	35	36	37	38	39	40
41	42	43	44	45	46	47	48	49	50
51	52	53	54	55	56	57	58	59	60
61	62	63	64	65	66	67	68	69	70
71	72	73	74	75	76	77	78	79	80
81	82	83	84	85	86	87	88	89	90
91	92	93	94	95	96	97	98	99	100

SET SEARCH

To identify numbers that belong to a particular set or sequence, for instance multiples, factors, primes, square numbers, triangular numbers.

†† *Whole-class introduction followed by individual work and a whole-class plenary.*

🕐 *Introduction 5–10 minutes; main activity 15–20 minutes; plenary 10 15 minutes; total 30–45 minutes.*

Previous skills/knowledge needed

It is assumed that children will have already been introduced to sets of special numbers such as prime numbers, square numbers, triangular numbers, multiples, factors, and so on.

Key background information

During Key Stage Two, children are introduced to a wide range of terminology associated with sets and sequences of special numbers. This activity provides an opportunity to revise or reinforce such work.

Preparation

Make copies of photocopiable page 105 so that there is one for each child.

Resources

Photocopiable page 105, paper, pencils, board/flip chart. For the extension activity – squared paper.

What to do

Introduction

Use the introduction to revise earlier work on sets and sequences of special numbers. Ask questions such as: *Can anyone tell me what the multiples of seven are? Who can explain what a factor is? Who can remember what a prime number is?* and so on. Use examples and further questions to explain these terms. Similarly, ask the children to explain and give examples of square numbers and triangular numbers. Both of these can be explained by drawing arrangements of dots on the board as shown below.

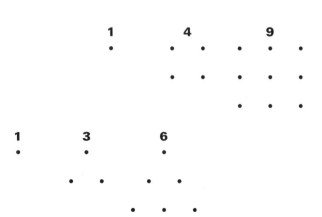

Main activity

Give each child a sheet of paper and a copy of photocopiable page 105 and explain that the sets or sequences of numbers listed down the left-hand side (apart from one) can be found somewhere on the grid by reading across the rows, down the columns or along the diagonals. Ask the children to find each one and then to draw a ring around it on the grid. They should also record each set or sequence on the separate sheet of paper. This will allow you to check the children's work.

Plenary

Start by asking the children which one of the sets or sequences could not be found on the grid (multiples of 8). Next, ask individual children to read out the sets and sequences which can be found on the grid. In the case of a sequence you could ask children to give three or four additional numbers beyond those listed on the grid. Also use the plenary as an opportunity to praise those children who have made their own set search grid (see 'Suggestion(s) for extension' below) and show these to the rest of the class.

Suggestion(s) for extension

Ask those children who complete the initial task to produce a set search grid of their own on a piece of squared paper and pass it on to someone else to complete.

Suggestion(s) for support

Give less able children a sheet listing the actual numbers in each set or sequence that can be found on the grid. Other pupils could be given additional aids to help them work out the numbers in each set or sequence before they look for them on the grid, for example having access to a multiplication grid will help them identify multiples, or drawing sequences of dots like those shown below left will help them to identify square and triangular numbers.

Assessment opportunities

The sets and sequences that the children record on their paper will provide assessment evidence of the children's knowledge of special numbers.

Display ideas

Display an enlarged version of the set search grid in the classroom and use it as a visual aid to recap work on sets and sequences of special numbers, perhaps as part of the introduction to other activities. Any set search grids the children have produced themselves could also be displayed.

Reference to photocopiable sheet

Photocopiable page 105 provides a number grid and lists various sets and sequences of numbers which the children have to locate inside the grid.

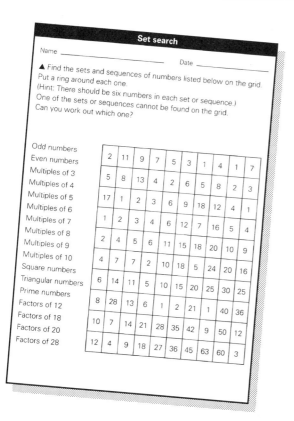

The diagram below shows the sixteen sets which can be found on the grid. The one which cannot be found is multiples of eight.

2	11	9	7	5	3	1	4	1	7
5	8	13	4	2	6	5	8	2	3
17	1	2	3	6	9	18	12	4	1
1	2	3	4	6	12	7	16	5	4
2	4	5	6	11	15	18	20	10	9
4	7	7	2	10	18	5	24	20	16
6	14	11	5	10	15	20	25	30	25
8	28	13	6	1	2	21	1	40	36
10	7	14	21	28	35	42	9	50	12
12	4	9	18	27	36	45	63	60	3

UPS AND DOWNS

To identify quickly numbers that belong to a particular set or sequence.

†† *Whole-class introduction followed by a game in pairs or small groups and a whole-class plenary.*

⏲ *Introduction 5–10 minutes; main activity 15–20 minutes; plenary 10–15 minutes; total 30–45 minutes.*

Previous skills/knowledge needed

It is assumed that children will have already been introduced to sets and sequences of special numbers such as prime numbers, square numbers, triangular numbers, multiples, factors and so on.

Key background information

This activity, like the previous one, 'Set search', provides children with an opportunity to revise and consolidate earlier work on sets and sequences of special numbers. You can be selective in terms of the sets or sequences you want the children to focus on, for example, they could focus on just multiples. In this way the activity can be used as a way of introducing particular special numbers. The main activity is a snakes and ladders type game but sets and sequences of special numbers are used instead of the snakes and ladders. For example, 'multiples of 5' might represent the snakes and 'square numbers' might represent the ladders. If a player lands on a multiple of 5 he or she must move back to the previous multiple of five, and if the player lands on a square number he or she moves forward to the next square number.

Preparation

For the main activity each pair or small group will need a snakes and ladders type playing board. Photocopiable page 106 can be used to produce these although ideally it will need to be enlarged so that the squares can accommodate a counter or other playing piece. The playing board could be enlarged onto card or laminated to make it more durable.

Each pair or small group will also need two small pieces of card indicating the two sets or sequences that are to be used to represent the snakes and the ladders. Each piece of card will identify a particular set or sequence. Here are some examples of the sorts of things you could write on the cards.

Multiples of 5	Factors of 90
Multiples of 6	Factors of 96
Multiples of 7	Factors of 100
Multiples of 8	Factors of 108
Multiples of 9	
Multiples of 10	Square numbers
Counting in 10s starting at 3	Triangular numbers
Counting in 5s starting at 2	Prime Numbers

The cards must be clearly marked either 'Up' or 'Down' to indicate whether a set or sequence represents the ladders or the snakes. An alternative is to colour-code the cards, for example green could be used for the 'Up' cards and pink for the 'Down' cards. Any given set or sequence can be used on both types of cards, for example 'Square numbers' could be on an 'Up' card for some children and on a 'Down' card for others. Make sure that the cards are matched to the ability of the children or match the chosen focus of the lesson.

Resources
Photocopiable page 106, cards (as described in 'Preparation'), six-sided dice (one per pair or group), counters, paper, pencils.

What to do
Introduction
Recap earlier work on sets and sequences of special numbers. Ask questions such as: *Can anyone tell me what the multiples of nine are? Who can explain what a factor is? Who can remember what a prime number is?* and so on. Use examples and further questions to aid understanding of these terms. Similarly, ask the children to explain and give examples of square numbers and triangular numbers (see the preceding activity 'Set search' for advice on how to explain these).

Main activity
Give out a copy of the playing board, one 'Up' card, one 'Down' card and a six-sided dice to each pair or small group, and a counter to each pupil. Explain to the children that the game is similar to 'Snakes and ladders' but this time special numbers are used instead of the snakes and ladders. Use one of the 'Up' cards and one of the 'Down' cards to explain how these are used.

Tell the children to watch carefully while the other children are having their turn so that any mistakes (or cheating) can be spotted and corrected. You might want the children to record their ups and downs on paper. For example, a child who lands on a square number (25) and moves on to the next square number (36) could record this as:

25 → 36

Similarly, if the child lands on a multiple of 9 (63) and moves back to the previous multiple of 9 (54) he or she could record this as:

63 → 54

Pupils could also divide their sheet of paper into two labelled columns, recording the 'ups' in one column and the 'downs' in the other.

Plenary
Use the plenary to reinforce the children's knowledge of sets and sequences of special numbers. Hold up one of the cards used during the main activity and ask the children to call out, in order, the numbers in that set or sequence. Start with one of the easier cards and repeat this with others of increasing difficulty.

Suggestion(s) for extension
Give able children the more challenging sets and sequences, for example square and triangular numbers.

Suggestion(s) for support
Allow less able children to use sets and sequences suited to their ability. Before playing the game, children could shade the numbers on the playing board that belong to the two sets or sequences they are going to use. The 'Up' numbers could be shaded in one colour and the 'Down' numbers in another. This will help them to quickly identify the numbers during the game.

Assessment opportunities
By asking pupils to record their 'ups' and 'downs' on paper you will be able to check their knowledge of special numbers.

Reference to photocopiable sheet
Photocopiable page 106 shows a number grid. The children play a game similar to 'Snakes and ladders' but instead of snakes and ladders the children use particular sets or sequences of numbers to move around the board.

FIBONACCI TOWERS

To follow simple rules to generate number sequences. To identify and explain the patterns in number sequences.

†† *Whole-class introduction followed by individual work and a whole-class plenary.*

🕐 *Introduction 5–10 minutes; main activity 25–30 minutes; plenary 15–20 minutes; total 45–60 minutes.*

Previous skills/knowledge needed

Children will need to be able to carry out arithmetic, using a calculator if necessary, be familiar with decimals in the context of a calculator display, and understand terminology such as 'multiples'.

Key background information

The Fibonacci sequence is named after the Italian mathematician Leonardo of Pisa who lived during the 12th century and was better known as Fibonacci. The first two numbers in the sequence are both 1. Subsequent numbers are found by adding the two previous numbers. The third number is therefore $1 + 1 = 2$, the fourth is $1 + 2 = 3$, the fifth is $2 + 3 = 5$ and so on. The first eight numbers in the sequence are: 1, 1, 2, 3, 5, 8, 13, 21.

This activity introduces children to the Fibonacci sequence and other similar sequences and asks them to investigate some of the properties.

Preparation

Make copies of photocopiable pages 107 and 108 so that there is one copy of both sheets for each child, although some pupils may not get as far as the second sheet. You may like to photocopy pages 107 and 108 back-to-back, thus creating a double-sided page, to reduce photocopying costs.

Resources

Photocopiable pages 107 and 108, calculators, paper, pencils, coloured pencils, board/flip chart.

What to do

Introduction

Write the first five numbers in the Fibonacci sequence on the board and say to the children: *Can anyone work out what the next number in the sequence is?* You might need to give a few clues, for example: *Try adding* or *What is 1 plus 1? What is 1 plus 2?* Write on the board any correct answers which the children provide but do not ask for explanations just yet. See if different children can provide the next few numbers. Repeat this until you have written three or four numbers on the board. Then ask the children to explain how the sequence is formed. Finally, tell the children the name of the sequence (write it on the board) and provide them with a little bit of background information.

Main activity

Give out copies of photocopiable sheet 107 and ask the children to work through it on their own. Explain any questions or instructions which are not clear and provide individual assistance when necessary. Give pupils a copy of photocopiable page 108 when they have completed page 107.

Children will definitely need to use calculators for questions 7 and 8 and you might want to allow them to use calculators when working out the numbers in the sequences. However, if you want to use this as an opportunity for pupils to practise non-calculator arithmetic then only give out the calculators after the children have completed questions 1 to 6.

Plenary

Use this time to discuss the answers to the questions and instructions on the sheets and the conclusions reached by the children. Start by asking pupils to call out the first twenty numbers in the Fibonacci sequence (question 1) and to each check this against what is written on their sheets. Then ask about the shadings of even numbers (every third number is even), multiples of three (every fourth number) and multiples of five (every fifth number).

Next, discuss the shadings for Tower 2. Ask the children about the shadings of the even numbers in this column

by saying: *Is every third number in Tower 2 even?* and *Did anyone get a different pattern of shading?* If some pupils answer 'Yes' to this second question, ask them to describe the shading and to tell you the numbers in the first two boxes of Tower 2. Record these on the board and repeat this for all pupils who answered 'Yes' to the second question. Ask the children what they notice about these starting numbers (they should all be even numbers). Hopefully, some children will be able to spot that when the two starting numbers are both even, the resulting sequence comprises only even numbers. Some pupils might be able to explain why (when you add two even numbers you always get an even answer).

Similarly, discuss the shadings of multiples of three for Tower 2. Regardless of the two starting numbers every fourth number after the first multiple of three should also be a multiple of three. The shadings of multiples of five is not so straightforward. Some starting numbers produce a sequence in which every fifth number is a multiple of five while others produce a sequence with no multiples of five at all.

Finally discuss the answers to questions 7 and 8. The result of dividing any number by the previous number gets closer and closer to 1.62 as you progress through the sequence. This is true regardless of the starting numbers.

Suggestion(s) for extension

Ask children to draw additional towers on a piece of paper, and to use different starting numbers of their own choice. These can be used to investigate the shadings further and will help pupils to spot the patterns and make generalizations.

Suggestion(s) for support

Some children might benefit from access to a calculator throughout the activity. They might also need reminding about how to check for divisibility by 2, 3 and 5.

Assessment opportunities

The children's completed photocopiable sheets will provide an insight into their ability to generate sequences correctly and to spot patterns in the sequences. Also, listen carefully to the children's responses during the plenary. Some may be capable of explaining the patterns and making generalizations, for example regarding the relationship between the starting numbers and the shadings of even numbers.

Opportunities for IT

Fibonacci and other adding sequences can be demonstrated easily using a spreadsheet by following these instructions:

Enter the number 1 into cells A1 and A2.
Enter the formula =A1+A2 into cell A3.

Use the copy and paste facilities or the fill down facility to copy the contents of cell A3 into cells A4 to A20.

The Fibonacci sequence should appear in column A. Different numbers can be entered in the top two cells and the other numbers will change accordingly. The spreadsheet can be used to aid the discussions during the plenary or used by individual children to investigate these sorts of sequences further.

Display ideas

The children's shaded towers can be displayed under appropriate headings such as 'These starting numbers produce multiples of five' and 'These starting numbers do not produce multiples of five.'

Reference to photocopiable sheets

Photocopiable pages 107 and 108 both provide two towers and a number of questions and instructions. The children have to fill in the towers using the principle of the Fibonacci sequence and then answer questions about the patterns they observe.

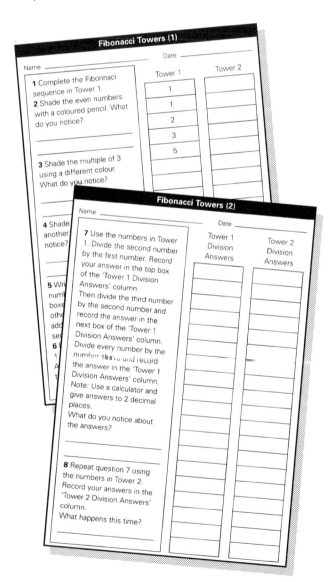

PALINDROMES

To understand the meaning of 'palindrome'. To identify numbers which belong to a particular set or sequence. To use the facilities of a calculator effectively to investigate special numbers.

†† *Whole-class introduction followed by individual work and a whole-class plenary.*

⏲ *Introduction 15–20 minutes; main activity 20–25 minutes; plenary 10–15 minutes; total 45–60 minutes.*

Madam, I'm Adam

Previous skills/knowledge needed

It is assumed that children will have already been introduced to sets and sequences of special numbers such as multiples, prime numbers, square numbers, triangular numbers, and so on.

Key background information

A palindrome is a number, word or sentence which reads the same backwards as it does forwards, for example the number 34743 and the word 'rotavator' are both palindromic. Examples of palindromic sentences include 'Madam, I'm Adam' and 'If I had a hi-fi'. This activity introduces children to palindromes and uses them to revise work on sets and sequences of special numbers such as multiples, square numbers, triangular numbers and prime numbers. The activity also encourages children to use a calculator effectively to investigate these numbers.

Preparation

Make copies of photocopiable page 109 so that there is one for each child. Also investigate how the constant function operates on the calculators you are using. For example, if you want to generate multiples of seven you will probably need to press:

But on some older calculators it is:

Resources

Photocopiable page 109, calculators, pencils, paper, board/flip chart.

What to do

Introduction

Start by revising earlier work on special numbers. Ask questions such as: *Can anyone tell me what the multiples of six are? Who can remember what a prime number is? What are the first five square numbers? What is a triangular number?* and so on. Discuss and explain all of these types of numbers (see the earlier activity 'Set search' for advice on how to explain square and triangular numbers).

Next discuss how a calculator can be used to generate or find these special numbers. Say to the children: *How can I produce multiples of seven using the calculator?* Some pupils may be aware of the constant function and so be able to explain it to you, otherwise explain it yourself. Give out the calculators and allow the children to practise using the constant function to generate multiples. Ask pupils how the calculator can be used to generate square numbers (simply multiply any number by itself) and also to check whether or not a given number is a square number (the easiest way is to use the square root key). Write two numbers on the board, for example 361 and 429, and use the calculator to check whether or not they are square numbers.

Move on to triangular numbers by asking pupils how these can be generated quickly using a calculator (use repeated addition: 1 + 2 + 3 + 4). Then ask how the calculator can be used to check whether or not a given number is a prime number. Write a number on the board, for example 187, and ask how you can check to find out whether or not it is prime. The only way is to try to find factors by dividing by 2, then by 3, then by 4 and so on (187 is not prime because it is divisible by 11 and 17). You might want to recap earlier work on divisibility, for example 187 is not divisible by 2 because the last digit is odd, it is not divisible by 5 because the last digit is not five or zero, and so on.

Write a few palindromic words on the board such as 'mum', 'pop', 'radar' and 'kayak'. Ask the children if they can spot what is special about these words. When they have noticed what it is ask them to think of other examples. Write these on the board and check that they are in fact palindromic. Explain that numbers can be palindromes and ask pupils to provide some examples. Write these on the board. Ask whether anyone has a palindromic telephone number or a palindromic house number.

Main activity

Give out a copy of photocopiable page 109 and a calculator to each child and ask the children to answer the questions.

Plenary

Go through the answers on the photocopiable sheet by asking individual children to call out their answers. Record some of the numbers on the board to demonstrate that they are palindromic. Ensure that some of the higher numbers, used by those children who carried out the extension activities, are recorded on the board so that all the children have an opportunity to see and discuss them. Also, ask some pupils to explain how they used the calculator to find a particular solution.

Suggestion(s) for extension

Ask those children who complete the questions to work through them again to find an additional solution to each one. Alternatively, ask more able children to find several solutions to each question from the outset. You could also impose constraints on some pupils, for example 'You must not use two-digit numbers' or 'Try to find solutions which have four or more digits'.

Suggestion(s) for support

The questions in the first section of the photocopiable sheet (those involving multiples) are fairly straightforward and so should be accessible to all pupils with the aid of the constant function of a calculator.

Assessment opportunities

During the main activity, ask the children to explain how they found a particular answer. The responses will provide an insight into their understanding of special numbers and their ability to use the facilities of a calculator effectively.

Opportunities for IT

ICT includes electronic calculators as well as computers and other types of hardware. By encouraging children to use the facilities of a calculator effectively this activity is therefore contributing to their ICT capability.

Display ideas

Palindromic numbers, words and sentences can form the basis of an interesting display. The numbers can be arranged under headings such as 'Palindromic primes', 'Palindromic square numbers' and so on. New numbers can be added to the lists as they are discovered by pupils over a period of time.

Reference to photocopiable sheet

Photocopiable page 109 reinforces work on palindromes by setting the children various palindromic problems which they must attempt to work out with the aid of a calculator.

There are an infinite number of solutions to all of the questions. The first ten solutions (in some cases the first five) to each question are provided on the opposite page.

Palindromes

Name _____ Date _____

Madam, I'm Adam

1 Find and write a palindrome which is
- a multiple of 3 _____
- a multiple of 4 _____
- a multiple of 5 _____
- a multiple of 6 _____
- a multiple of 7 _____
- a multiple of 8 _____
- a multiple of 9 _____
- a multiple of 11 _____
- a multiple of 12 _____

Why do you think there are no palindromes which are multiples of 10?

_____

2 Find and write down a palindrome which is
- a square number _____
- a triangular number _____
- a prime number _____

3 Find and write down two palindromes which have
- a difference of 2 _____
- a difference of 10 _____
- a difference which is a palindrome _____
- a product which is a palindrome _____

Palindromic multiples of 3:
33, 66, 99, 111, 141, 171, 222, 252, 282 and 303.
Palindromic multiples of 4:
44, 88, 212, 232, 252, 272, 292, 404, 424 and 444.
Palindromic multiples of 5:
55, 505, 515, 525, 535, 545, 555, 565, 575 and 585
Palindromic multiples of 6:
66, 222, 252, 282, 414, 444, 474, 606, 636 and 666.
Palindromic multiples of 7:
77, 161, 252, 343, 434, 525, 595, 616, 686 and 707.
Palindromic multiples of 8:
88, 232, 272, 424, 464, 616, 656, 696, 808 and 848.
Palindromic multiples of 9:
99, 171, 252, 333, 414, 585, 666, 747, 828 and 909.
Palindromic multiples of 11:
11, 22, 33, 44, 55, 66, 77, 88, 99 and 121.
Palindromic multiples of 12:
252, 444, 636, 696, 828, 888, 2112, 2772, 4224 and 4884.

Palindromic square numbers:
121, 484, 676, 10201 and 12321.
Palindromic triangular numbers:
55, 66, 171, 595 and 666.
Palindromic prime numbers:
11, 101, 131, 151, 181, 191, 313, 353, 373 and 383.

Two palindromes with a difference of 2 are 999 and 1001.
There are many pairs of palindromes with a difference of
10, for example 101 and 111, 121 and 131, 141 and 151,
and so on.
There are many pairs of palindromes whose difference is
a palindrome, for example pairs which differ by 11 such
as 22 and 33, and pairs which differ by 111 such as 222
and 333.
There are many pairs of palindromes with a palindromic
product, for example the product of 22 and 111 is 2442.

MATHS WITH A CALENDAR

*To identify patterns and relationships in number
grids. To practise mental and pencil and paper
calculation skills.*

✝✝ *Whole-class introduction followed by individual
work and a whole-class plenary.*

🕐 *Introduction 5–10 minutes; main activity 25–30
minutes; plenary 15–20 minutes; total 45–60
minutes.*

Previous skills/knowledge needed
Children will need to be able to carry out arithmetic
involving whole numbers up to 100 without a calculator.

Key background information
This activity focuses on two very important aspects of
number work: the development of efficient arithmetic skills
and the ability to spot patterns and relationships in
numbers. The two are very closely linked in that each can
assist in the development of the other and both are
essential in problem-solving work. For example, by spotting
that the middle number in a sequence of three numbers
is always one-third of the total, children can use this
knowledge to find sequences which have a given total or
to explain that some totals are not possible.

Preparation
Make copies of photocopiable pages 110 and 111 so that
there is one copy of each sheet per pupil. (You may like to
photocopy the pages back-to-back, thus creating a double-
sided page, to reduce photocopying costs.) The sheets
show one month of a calendar which the children are
required to answer questions about. You might prefer to
make copies of a calendar for the current month or the
whole year and ask children to use this instead of, or as

well as, the calendar on the sheet. However, you will need to check that it is possible to answer all of the questions on the sheet using the current calendar.

Resources
Photocopiable pages 110 and 111, paper, pencils, board/ flip chart.

What to do
Introduction
Revise some of the terminology used on photocopiable pages 110 and 111, for example the words 'row', 'column', 'horizontal', 'vertical' and 'diagonal'. One possible way of doing this is to write several numbers on the board, arranged into rows and columns, and to ask the children questions about them, for example: *Tell me three numbers which are in a line vertically* and *What is the sum of the first two numbers in the second row?*

Main activity
Give each child a copy of photocopiable page 110 and ask them to complete the questions using the calendar on the sheet. When the children have completed sheet 110 they can move on to sheet 111.

Plenary
Go through the answers to the first five questions on photocopiable page 110. Record the answers to questions 3, 4 and 5 on the board under appropriate headings such as 'Sum of 75' and use these to help the children spot the answer to question 6, that is, that the middle number is always one-third of the total. In addition you could ask: *Is this true for any three numbers in a line?* and ask the children to provide as many examples as they can to justify their answers.

Ask the children to give the answers to questions 7 and 8. Can anyone explain why the difference between the smallest and biggest numbers in the square is always 8? One possible explanation is that the smallest is always in the top-left corner, the biggest is always in the bottom-right corner, and in moving from one to the other you must move down a row (add 7) and across to the right (add 1). It could also be explained in terms of what the calendar actually represents – the latest date in the square is one week and a day after the earliest.

Ask the children to use examples to explain the answer to question 9. Record some of the 2 by 2 groups of four numbers on the board to assist the explanations, particularly if there are a number of children in the class who did not answer question 9.

Finally, pose this new question: *Can you spot the connection between the top-left number in a 2 by 2 square and the sum of the four numbers?* Use the 2 by 2 groups of numbers which are already on the board, highlighting the top-left number in each one and also writing the sum

of the four numbers at the side. Give a clue if necessary, such as: *Try multiplying by four.* An able child might spot that if you multiply the top-left number by four and then add 16, you get the sum of the four numbers. Try explaining this to the pupils by first drawing an empty 2 × 2 grid on the board. Write a question mark in the top-left cell to represent a mystery number so that the grid looks like this.

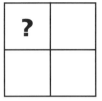

Ask pupils what they can tell you about the top-right number compared to the mystery number (it is one more) and then write '? + 1' in the top-right cell. Similarly, ask pupils what they can tell you about the bottom-left and bottom-right numbers compared to the mystery number (they are seven and eight more respectively). Complete the grid so that it looks like this.

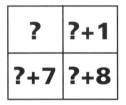

Then write down the sum of the four cells.

$$? + ?+1 + ?+7 + ?+8$$

This can be thought of as four lots of the mystery number plus 16 and written as:

$$4 \times ? + 16$$

So regardless of which 2 by 2 group is used, the total is always four times the top-left number plus 16.

Suggestion(s) for extension

After the children have completed the photocopiable sheet they could attempt the questions again using a different calendar, for example the current month. Ask the children to investigate whether questions 1 to 5 can be answered using any month of any year or whether only certain months can be used. They could also investigate whether their findings in questions 6 to 9 are repeated for other months. Another possibility is to answer questions 3 to 9 using a 100-square.

Suggestion(s) for support

Many of the questions on photocopiable page 110 should be accessible to all pupils although the questions which involve identifying relationships (questions 6, 8 and 9) may prove too tricky for some. Be selective therefore in the questions you ask the children to attempt. Pupils could also tackle selected questions, for example questions 3, 4, 5 and 7, using different calendars and a 100-square.

	A	B	C	D	E	F	G	H	I
1	Mon	Tues	Weds	Thurs	Fri	Sat	Sun		
2			1	2	3	4	5		
3	6	7	8	9	10	11	12		
4	13	14	15	16	17	18	19		
5	20	21	22	23	24	25	26		
6	27	28	29	30	31				
7									
8									
9									
10									
11									

Assessment opportunities

The children's written work will provide valuable evidence of their ability to carry out arithmetic without the aid of a calculator (questions 1, 2, 3, 4, 5 and 7) and also their ability to identify patterns and relationships (questions 6, 8 and 9). Also make a mental note of the children's responses during the plenary, particularly when relationships are being discussed.

Opportunities for IT

Row and column totals of number grids, including calendars, can be obtained quickly using a spreadsheet. For example, the calendar on the photocopiable sheet could be entered on a spreadsheet as illustrated above.

If the formula = SUM(A2:A6) is entered into cell A8 the sum of the first column will be displayed in this cell. Similarly, if the formula = SUM(A2:G2) is entered into cell

I2 the sum of the first row will be displayed. The copy and paste facilities can be used to copy these formulae into adjacent cells so that all row and column totals are displayed.

Display ideas

Enlarged versions of several different calendars and other number grids can be displayed on the wall together with a set of targets similar to those in questions 3, 4, 5 and 7 on the photocopiable sheets. Pupils can attempt to find the solutions during any spare moments they have during the day. A new set of questions can be put up on the wall every few days.

Reference to photocopiable sheets

Photocopiable pages 110 and 111 depict a calendar month and related questions and instructions which the children have to complete.

The answers are as follows.

1 The sum of the numbers in the first column is 66. The fourth column (Thursday) has a sum of 80.

2 The sum of the numbers in the top row is 15. The bottom row has a sum of 145.

3 24, 25 and 26 (and also on a 100-square).

4 8, 15 and 22 (5, 15 and 25 on a 100-square).

5 10, 18 and 26 or 24, 18 and 12 (7, 18 and 29 or 27, 18 and 9 on a 100-square).

6 The middle number is one-third of the sum of the three numbers (also true on a 100-square).

7 11, 12, 18 and 19 (impossible on a 100-square).

8 The difference is always 8 (11 on a 100-square).

9 The difference is always 7 (10 on a 100-square).

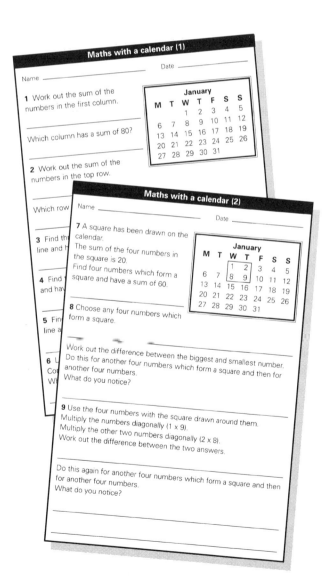

NEIGHBOURS

To identify patterns in sums of consecutive numbers. To add two or more numbers up to 100 without a calculator.

†† *Whole-class introduction followed by individual work and a whole-class plenary.*

⏱ *Introduction 5–10 minutes; main activity 30–35 minutes; plenary 10–15 minutes; total 45–60 minutes.*

Previous skills/knowledge needed
Children will need to be able to add two or more numbers up to 100.

Key background information
This activity has a simple starting point and, in terms of mathematical skills, requires children to do no more than add one and two-digit numbers. However, it offers much potential for exploring patterns and relationships in the number system. It is important that pupils develop both the ability to calculate effectively and to identify number patterns, since each of these two areas supports the other. Both are covered in this activity.

Preparation
Make copies of photocopiable page 104 so that there is one for each child.

Resources
Photocopiable page 104, paper, coloured pencils.

What to do
Introduction
Write the word 'consecutive' on the board and ask if anyone can explain what it means. Include numbers in the discussion by asking the children to tell you three consecutive numbers. (You might like to use the expression 'three neighbours' to mean 'three consecutive numbers'.) Also, ask pupils to quickly work out the sum of the three consecutive numbers they have provided. This can be used as an opportunity to practise mental calculation skills by asking the children to give you as many examples as possible of three consecutive numbers together with their sum.

Now reverse the process. Provide a number which is the sum of three consecutive numbers and ask the children to work out what the numbers are. For example, if you called out '24', a correct response would be '7, 8 and 9'. If a child responds incorrectly then ask him or her to quickly add the three numbers together and offer a further prompt such as: *So are your numbers too big or too small?* You could also do this for two or four consecutive numbers so that the questions you ask are matched to the abilities of individual pupils.

Main activity

Ask the children to tell you a number which can be made by adding two consecutive numbers (or two 'neighbours') and record it on the board. Repeat this until you have two or three examples. Hand out the coloured pencils and the copies of photocopiable page 104 and pose this question: *Which numbers up to 100 can be made by adding two consecutive numbers?* Explain that you want the children to investigate this using the 100-square on the photocopiable sheet. Stress that they must record their work carefully by shading in all of the numbers that can be made. It might be necessary to explain that zero can be used as one of the consecutive numbers, for example 1 can be made by adding 0 and 1.

After the children have completed the initial task, ask them to investigate which numbers up to 100 can be made by adding three consecutive numbers. Again, these can be shaded on the 100-square, this time using a different colour. Further stages the children could investigate are which numbers can be made by adding four numbers, five numbers, six numbers, and so on. Pose this final question: *Are there any numbers up to 100 which cannot be made by adding consecutive numbers?*

Plenary

Discuss the numbers which can be made by adding two neighbours, three neighbours, four neighbours and so on. For each one, ask the children to tell you the numbers which can be made and also to explain the pattern or sequence in their own words. The shadings on the 100-square should help them to identify the number patterns.

Discuss the final question posed above: *Are there any numbers up to 100 which cannot be made by adding consecutive numbers?* If the class is able to answer this question then record the answers on the board (2, 4, 8, 16, 32 and 64) and ask the children to describe this sequence in their own words (a doubling sequence).

Suggestion(s) for extension

The main activity offers much work even for the most able children but if anyone answers the final question then offer further extension work by asking: *Can the missing numbers be made if we allow the use of negative numbers?*

Suggestion(s) for support

The early stages of the main activity should be accessible to all children although you might feel that it is appropriate for some pupils to use a calculator so that they can focus on

investigating the number patterns without having to worry about the arithmetic.

Assessment opportunities

During the main activity ask the children to explain in their own words the patterns in the numbers which can be made by adding two neighbours, three neighbours, and so on. This will indicate their ability to identify patterns and sequences. You might like to ask all pupils to write down a sentence describing each pattern so that you can assess all pupils against this particular learning objective.

Opportunities for IT

Sums of consecutive numbers can be generated easily using a spreadsheet. Enter the numbers 0 to 50 into column A. Into cell B2, enter the formula = A1+A2 and use the copy and paste facility to enter similar formulae into the cells below. This should produce numbers which can be made by adding two consecutive numbers. Into cell C3, enter the formula = A1+A2+A3 and again copy and paste this into the cells below. This should produce numbers which can be made by adding three consecutive numbers. Similar formulae can be entered into cells D3 (enter = A1+A2+A3+A4 or alternatively =SUM(A1:A4)), E5 (enter = A1+A2+A3+A4+A5 or =SUM(A1:A5)), and so on. The top left portion of the spreadsheet should look like this.

	A	B	C	D	E	F
1	0					
2	1	1				
3	2	3	3			
4	3	5	6	6		
5	4	7	9	10	10	
6	5	9	12	14	15	15
7	6	11	15	18	20	21
8	7	13	18	22	25	27
9	8	15	21	26	30	33
10	9	17	24	30	35	39
11	10	19	27	34	40	45

Display ideas

Shaded 100-squares (only one type of shading per sheet) can be displayed under appropriate headings, for example 'These numbers can be made from two neighbours', 'These numbers can be made from three neighbours', and so on.

Reference to photocopiable sheet

Photocopiable page 104 shows a 100-square. The children investigate which numbers up to 100 can be made by adding consecutive numbers.

Two neighbours produces 1, 3, 5, 7, 9, ..., 99 (counting in 2s).

Three neighbours produces 3, 6, 9, 12, 15, ..., 99 (counting in 3s).

Four neighbours produces 6, 10, 14, 18, 22, ..., 98 (counting in 4s).

Five neighbours produces 10, 15, 20, 25, 30, ..., 100 (counting in 5s).

Six neighbours produces 15, 21, 27, 33, 39, ..., 99 (counting in 6s).

Seven neighbours produces 21, 28, 35, 42, 49, ..., 98 (counting in 7s).

Eight neighbours produces 28, 36, 44, 52, 60, ..., 100 (counting in 8s).

Nine neighbours produces 36, 45, 54, 63, 72, ..., 99 (counting in 9s).

Ten neighbours produces 45, 55, 65, 75, 85, 95 (counting in 10s).

Eleven neighbours produces 55, 66, 77, 88, 99 (counting in 11s).

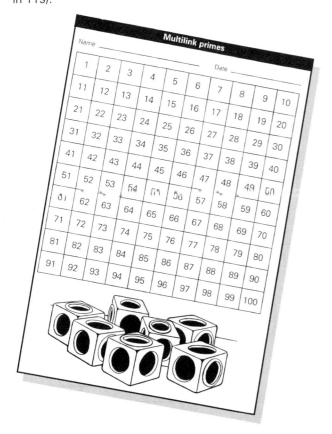

Twelve neighbours produces 66, 78, 90 (counting in 12s).
Thirteen neighbours produces 78, 91 (counting in 13s).
Fourteen neighbours produces 91.

It is not possible to make 2, 4, 8, 16, 32 and 64.

If negative numbers are allowed then it is possible to make 2, 4, 8, 16, 32 and 64.
2 can be made using four neighbours (–1, 0, 1, 2).
4 can be made using eight neighbours (–3, –2, –1, 0, 1, 2, 3, 4).
Similarly, 8 can be made using 16 neighbours (from –7 to 8); 16 can be made using 32 neighbours (from –15 to 16); 32 can be made using 64 neighbours (from –31 to 32) and 64 can be made using 128 neighbours (from –63 to 64).

MATCHSTICK PATTERNS

To identify and continue visual patterns. To generate and continue number sequences associated with a visual pattern.

†† *Whole-class introduction followed by individual work and a whole-class plenary.*

⏱ *Introduction 5–10 minutes; main activity 25–30 minutes; plenary 15–20 minutes; total 45–60 minutes.*

Previous skills/knowledge needed

It is assumed that children will have already done some work on identifying and continuing visual and numerical patterns.

Key background information

In this activity children are required to identify and continue visual patterns made from matchsticks and then to investigate the numerical patterns and relationships which exist. It is important that pupils are given an opportunity to develop these skills since they form the basis of future algebra work and can also be put to good use in problem-solving and investigative work.

Preparation

Draw these sequences of matchstick patterns on three large sheets of paper.

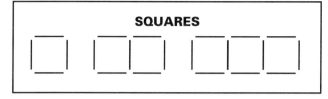

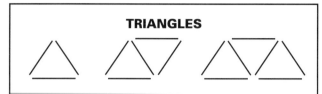

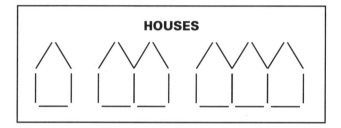

discussed during the introduction. The first three patterns can be copied from the large sheets of paper and the fourth pattern can be copied from the board. Pupils will have to work out the fifth and sixth patterns for themselves.

When some children have completed the initial task, stop the whole class and explain the next part of the activity. For each arrangement of matchsticks, pupils must count and record the number of shapes, the number of matchsticks and the number of joins (a join is where two or more matchsticks meet). Use some of the arrangements on the large sheets of paper to explain what must be counted and recorded, for example the first arrangement in the squares sequence has 1 shape (there is one square), 4 matchsticks and 4 joins. The second arrangement in the squares sequence has 2 shapes, 7 matchsticks and 6 joins.

When the children have completed the second stage of the activity, ask them to look for patterns in the numbers they have recorded. For example, can they see a pattern in the number of joins or in the number of matchsticks in each sequence? When they have identified these patterns they can use them to predict how many matchsticks and joins there will be in the seventh, eighth, ninth and tenth arrangement of each sequence.

Resources
Large sheets of paper displaying the matchstick patterns as described in 'Preparation' above, paper, pencils, board/flip chart.

What to do

Introduction
Display the first large sheet of paper on the wall (the one showing the squares) and explain to the children that the patterns have been made using matchsticks. (You might prefer to refer to them as pencils, straws or some other similar object.) Point to the first pattern and say: *This is the first pattern in the sequence.* Point to the second and say: *This is the second pattern in the sequence.* Finally point to the third and say: *This is the third pattern in the sequence.* Then ask a child to come out and draw the fourth pattern in the sequence on the board.

Repeat this process with the triangular arrangement and finally with the houses arrangement of matchsticks.

Main activity
Give out the paper and pencils and tell the children to draw the first six matchstick patterns in each of the sequences

Plenary
Use the plenary to work through and discuss the solutions to the main activity. Start by asking pupils to come out and draw the fifth and sixth arrangement in each sequence. Then move on to the numbers of shapes, matchsticks and joins in each arrangement. These could be recorded on the board in tables like those shown below.

SQUARES				TRIANGLES				HOUSES		
Shapes	Matches	Joins		Shapes	Matches	Joins		Shapes	Matches	Joins
1	4	4		1	3	3		1	5	5
2	7	6		2	5	4		2	9	8
3	10	8		3	7	5		3	13	11
4	13	10		4	9	6		4	17	14
5	16	12		5	11	7		5	21	17
6	19	14		6	13	8		6	25	20

This should enable most children to spot the patterns in the columns of numbers. Ask pupils to explain these patterns in their own words, particularly those pupils who did not progress to this stage during the main activity. Also, ask the children to use the number patterns to predict how many shapes, matches and joins there will be in the seventh, eighth, ninth and tenth arrangement of each sequence. These figures can be recorded by adding additional rows to the tables above.

Suggestion(s) for extension

Three matchstick sequences are described above but there are many other suitable sequences which could be investigated by pupils who complete the main activity. Here are a few possibilities which are slightly more challenging. These can be drawn on the board or on large sheets of paper so that pupils can copy them, continue each sequence, record the numbers of shapes, matches and joins, and finally look for patterns in the numbers.

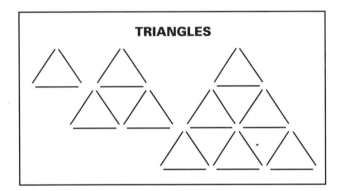

TRIANGLES

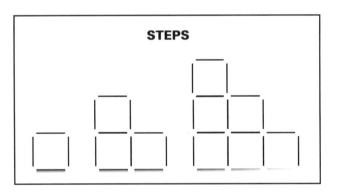

STEPS

The numbers in the first column of the triangles table are square numbers and the third column shows triangular numbers. The numbers in the second column go up by 3, then by 6, then by 9, then by 12, and so on.

The first column of the steps table shows triangular numbers. The numbers in the second column go up by 6, then by 8, then by 10, then by 12, and so on. The numbers in the third column go up by 4, then by 5, then by 6, then by 7, and so on.

Suggestion(s) for support

It might be appropriate for some pupils to make the patterns using practical apparatus (such as pencils, straws or matchsticks) before drawing them. All children should be capable of spotting and continuing the visual patterns and most should be capable of counting the numbers of shapes, matchsticks and joins.

Assessment opportunities

The children's written work will provide valuable evidence of their abilities to identify and continue visual shapes and the associated numerical patterns. Make a mental note of pupils' responses during the plenary, particularly from those who do not complete all stages of the main activity. Their responses may provide assessment evidence which does not exist in written form.

Display ideas

The visual nature of the work produced makes it ideal for displaying in the classroom. The matchstick patterns and the tables of number sequences can be displayed together.

TRIANGLES			STEPS		
Shapes	Matches	Joins	Shapes	Matches	Joins
1	3	3	1	4	4
4	9	6	3	10	8
9	18	10	6	18	13
16	30	15	10	28	19
25	45	21	15	40	26
36	63	28	21	54	34

ZOOM

To follow a set of instructions shown on a flow-chart. To use a calculator effectively. To identify number patterns in sets of results.

†† *Whole-class introduction followed by individual work and a whole-class plenary.*

🕐 *Introduction 10–15 minutes; main activity 25–30 minutes; plenary 10–15 minutes; total 45–60 minutes.*

Previous skills/knowledge needed

Pupils will need to be able to use a calculator to carry out arithmetic and have an understanding of decimals in the context of the calculator display.

Key background information

Access to a calculator enables children to work out quickly the answers to complex calculations and so free up time to concentrate on higher level skills such as identifying patterns and solving problems. In this activity the calculator is used to investigate the results of iterative methods, that is, a short sequence of calculations which is repeated over and over again, with the output of one iteration providing the input for the next. These outputs usually converge on a particular value.

Preparation

Draw this flow chart on a large sheet of paper or on the board.

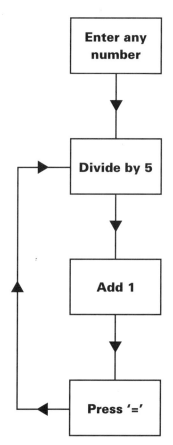

On a large sheet of paper make a copy of this table.

	DIVIDE BY				
	2	3	4	5	6
− 4					
− 3					
− 2					
− 1					
0					
+ 1					
+ 2					
+ 3					
+ 4					

Also ensure that there are enough calculators, one per pupil.

Resources

Calculators, paper, pencils, the flow chart and table as described in 'Preparation'.

What to do

Introduction

Draw the children's attention to the flow-chart and ask if anyone knows what it is called. Hopefully, someone will be able to tell you, otherwise provide the answer. Ask what a flow-chart is used for (to give a set of instructions) and what this particular flow-chart is telling them to do. Explain the instructions shown on the flow-chart, paying particular attention to what happens after the equals key is pressed. Explain that the cycle involving division and addition is repeated over and over again.

Give out the calculators and ask pupils to enter a starting number of their own choice. Talk them through the key-presses, slowly at first, but then let them work through more quickly. Tell them to look at the number in the display after the equals key is pressed each time and to watch how this number changes at the completion of each cycle.

After about a minute tell everyone to stop when they next press the equals key. Ask individual pupils to tell you the number in their display and record these on the board. You may like to use this as an opportunity to practise rounding skills by specifying that the numbers should be rounded to two or three decimal places. Ask the children what they notice about the numbers (everyone should have a number which is close to 1.25) and conclude by stating that, regardless of the starting number, everyone's answer has converged or 'zoomed-in' on 1.25. If you think it is necessary, tell the children to repeat the process using a different starting number, particularly if some pupils were not successful in following the instructions the first time.

Main activity

Tell the children that you now want them to investigate what happens if they change the number which is added each time (point to the 'Add 1' box on the flow-chart). Say to them: *I wonder what will happen to the final number if you add 2 each time, or add 3 each time, or add 4 each time?* Stress that they can choose any starting number but they must keep working through the flow-chart until

they are sure what the answer is converging or 'zooming-in' on. Give each child some paper and remind pupils to make a note of the number they add each time as well as the final number they 'zoom-in' on.

When pupils have tried adding 2, 3 and 4 (and possibly other numbers as well) ask them to try subtracting 1, subtracting 2, and subtracting 3 instead of adding. When they have explored several of the possibilities, ask them whether they can see any patterns in the results.

While the pupils are working, attach the table you prepared earlier to the wall so that everyone can see it clearly. Allow the children about 15 minutes to work on the main activity, then stop the class and bring the table to their attention. Point to the 'Divide by 5' column and explain that this is where you are going to summarize their results. Point to the cell where the 'Divide by 5' column and the '+ 1' row intersect and ask: *What number should I write in this cell?* If necessary provide a prompt by asking: *What number did you zoom in on when you divided by 5* (point to the column) *and added 1?* (point to the row). The pupils should tell you to write 1.25 in this cell. Ask the pupils to tell you other results they have found and write these in the 'Divide by 5' column. It is unlikely that anyone will have tried adding zero and so you will probably need to discuss this and possibly allow the children to try it out for themselves. You might want to ask: *Why do we get zero when we keep dividing by 5?* The completed table should look like the one at the top of the opposite page.

	DIVIDE BY				
	2	3	4	5	6
− 4				−5	
− 3				− 3.75	
− 2				− 2.5	
− 1				− 1.25	
0				0	
+ 1				1.25	
+ 2				2.5	
+ 3				3.75	
+ 4				5	

Finally, ask the children if they can see a pattern in the column of numbers and ask individuals to explain it in their own words.

As the next stage of the main activity, ask pupils to divide by numbers other than 5 so that the remaining columns of the table can be filled in. Refer children to the original flow-chart and explain that now they must repeat what they were doing earlier but this time divide by another number, for example 2 instead of 5. You could ask different groups of pupils to use different divisors, for example, one group divides by 2, another divides by 3, another divides by 4, and so on. Use the flow-chart to remind pupils that they can choose any starting number but they must keep working through the flow-chart until they are sure what the answer is 'zooming-in' on. When they have done this for 'add 1' they can investigate what happens when other numbers are added or subtracted.

Plenary

Ask pupils to call out their results so that the remaining cells in the table can be filled in (decimal answers can be rounded to two decimal places). The completed table should look like this.

	DIVIDE BY				
	2	3	4	5	6
− 4	− 8	− 6	− 6.33	− 5	− 4.8
− 3	− 6	− 4.5	− 5	− 3.75	− 3.6
− 2	− 4	− 3	− 2.67	− 2.5	− 2.4
− 1	− 2	− 1.5	− 1.33	− 1.25	− 1.2
0	0	0	0	0	0
+ 1	2	1.5	1.33	1.25	1.2
+ 2	4	3	2.67	2.5	2.4
+ 3	6	4.5	5	3.75	3.6
+ 4	8	6	6.33	5	4.8

Point to the first column and ask the children to explain the pattern in the results. Repeat this for the other columns of numbers. You might want to discuss the results of the extension activity described below and also investigate what happens if you divide by 1 each time (the final answer does not converge; it just gets bigger and bigger).

Suggestion(s) for extension

The main activity should pose a challenge for even the most able pupils but if some children do require extension work then ask them what they think will happen if they add or subtract numbers such as 1.5, 2.5, 3.5 and so on. Encourage them to predict first before trying it out.

Suggestion(s) for support

The main activity should be accessible to all pupils once they are fully aware of the instructions shown on the flow-chart. Some children might benefit from an adult helper in the early stages who can talk them through the key presses until they are fully confident.

Assessment opportunities

Observe pupils carefully throughout the lesson to check that they are following the flow-chart accurately and using the calculator correctly. During the main activity ask pupils whether they can spot any patterns in the results they are generating. Make a mental note of the children's responses during the plenary.

Opportunities for IT

A single column of a spreadsheet can be used to generate the same numbers as the flow-chart. Type any number (such as 37) into cell A1. Enter the formula =A1/5+1 into cell A2 and copy this down the column as far as cell A15. The spreadsheet should look like this.

	A	B
1	37	
2	8.4	
3	2.68	
4	1.536	
5	1.3072	
6	1.26144	
7	1.252288	
8	1.250457	
9	1.250091	
10	1.250018	
11	1.250003	
12	1.250001	
13	1.25	
14	1.25	
15	1.25	
16		

Try changing the starting number in cell A1. The sequence should converge on 1.25 regardless of the starting number. The formula which was copied down the column can be changed to, =A1/5+2 for example, to investigate the effect of changing the number which is added or subtracted. Similarly, the formula can be changed to, for example, =A1/3+1 in order to investigate the effect of changing the divisor.

Display ideas

Display the large sheets of paper showing the flow-chart and the results summary in the classroom.

TWELVE SQUARE CENTIMETRES

To draw shapes of a given area. To identify patterns and relationships in the numerical properties of shapes.

†† *Whole-class introduction followed by individual work and a whole-class plenary.*

🕐 *Introduction 10–15 minutes; main activity 25–30 minutes; plenary 10–15 minutes; total 45–60 minutes.*

Previous skills/knowledge needed

Children will need to have had some experience of investigating patterns and relationships and will need to be familiar with finding the areas of simple shapes using square centimetres.

Key background information

The first stage of this activity is open-ended, requiring pupils to make shapes of a given area. The second stage focuses on the patterns and relationships that exist among some of the physical features of the shapes which have been produced.

Preparation

Each child will need at least one sheet of square spotted paper for the main activity (use photocopiable page 101 if necessary). Those children who are able to produce a large number of shapes will require two, or possibly three, sheets.

Draw a few shapes on the board, labelled with their dimensions, so that they all have an area of 20 square centimetres. Use shapes which are within the capabilities of the pupils. Here are a few possibilities.

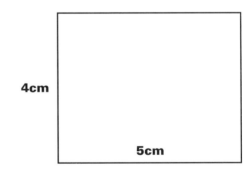

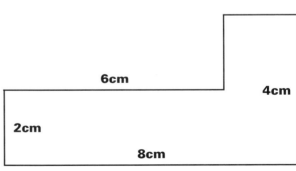

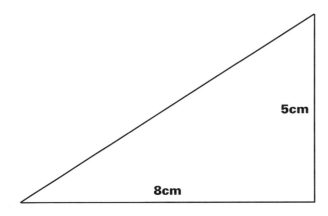

5cm

8cm

Resources
Sheets of square spotted paper (photocopiable page 101 optional), pencils, rulers.

What to do
Introduction
Recap earlier work on area by pointing to the first shape on the board and asking: *What is the area of this shape?* Encourage children to explain how they worked out their answer. Repeat this with the second shape. If you have used a shape like the second one shown on the opposite page you might like to start by asking pupils to work out the lengths of the sides which are not labelled before moving on to the area. When discussing the area you could consider the different methods which could be used to work it out. Some pupils may choose to divide the shape into two rectangles by drawing a vertical line. Some might do this using a horizontal line. A third option is to think of it as a large 4cm × 8cm rectangle with a smaller rectangle cut from it. Repeat this with the other shapes you have drawn on the board, again encouraging the pupils to discuss the possible methods which can be used to ascertain the area. Finish by asking one or two pupils to come out and sketch other shapes which have an area of exactly 20 square centimetres and discuss these.

Main activity
Give out the sheets of square spotted paper and explain to the children that they must draw as many different shapes as they can which all have an area of exactly 12 square centimetres.

Observe pupils carefully, providing appropriate encouragement but also watching out for any errors and misconceptions. For example, you might need to encourage able pupils to draw more complex shapes rather than relying on rectangles.

While the children are working, add spots to one or two of the drawings on the board so that they look as if they have been drawn on square spotted paper. Here are two of the earlier examples, complete with spots.

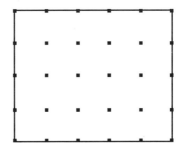

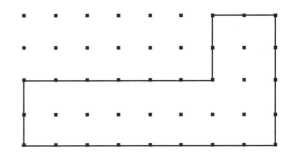

Allow the children about 10 to 15 minutes to carry out the main activity, then stop the class and ask them to look at the shapes on the board. Tell pupils that they are going to investigate the numbers of spots on the perimeter of their shapes and inside their shapes. Point to the first shape and ask: *How many spots are on the perimeter of this shape?* Discuss and explain this if necessary and record the answer beside or beneath the shape (there are 18 spots on the perimeter). Then ask: *How many spots are inside this shape?* Again record the answer on the board (there are 12 spots inside the shape). Repeat this for the second shape (there are 24 spots on the perimeter and 9 spots inside).

Explain to the children that they must now count the number of spots on the perimeter and the number of spots inside the shapes they have drawn. They should record their answers on the sheets, next to the shapes.

Again, observe pupils carefully watching for errors and misconception. A quick way of spotting errors is to remember that if you double the number of spots on the inside and add this to the number on the perimeter the answer should always be 26 (don't tell the pupils the rule just yet). If this is not true for a pupil's shape then they have either miscounted or the shape does not have an area of 12 square centimetres.

After about 5 or 10 minutes stop the class again and use a show of hands to find out what sorts of results pupils are coming up with. Ask questions such as: *Has anyone got a shape with more than 20 spots on the perimeter? What is the biggest number of spots you can get inside a shape? What is the smallest number?* and so on. Tell pupils to draw additional shapes which have combinations of spots different to those they have already.

Plenary
Start by asking questions such as: *What is the biggest number of spots you can have inside a shape? What is the smallest? What is the biggest number of spots you can have on the perimeter? What is the smallest?* and so on. These two examples illustrate the maximum and minimum numbers of spots on the inside and on the perimeter.

and *I wonder if it is possible to produce such a shape?* Some pupils might like to try this later (it is impossible).

Pupils might also notice that as the numbers in one column go up, the numbers in the other column go down. You can make this relationship more obvious by arranging the table of results in order, so that it looks like this.

Spots Inside	Spots on Perimeter
0	26
1	24
2	22
3	20
4	18
5	16
6	14
7	12
8	10
9	8
10	6
11	4

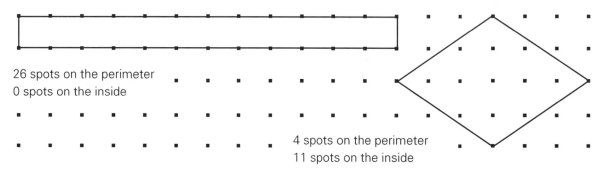

26 spots on the perimeter
0 spots on the inside

4 spots on the perimeter
11 spots on the inside

Next, record pupils' findings on the board. You could use a table like this.

Spots inside	Spots on perimeter

Ask pupils what they notice about the numbers in the table. Provide additional prompts and questions if necessary, for example: *What do you notice about all of the numbers in the second column?* (They should all be even numbers.) Follow this with questions such as *Did anyone produce a shape which has an odd number of spots on the perimeter?*

A final question, which some able pupils may be able to answer is: *Can you spot the rule connecting the number of spots on the inside with the number of spots on the perimeter?* (If you double the number of spots on the inside and add this to the number on the perimeter the answer should always be 26.)

Suggestion(s) for extension

Even the most able pupils should find this activity challenging. During the main activity encourage pupils to produce unusual shapes and to find shapes with different numbers of spots on the perimeter and on the inside. Pose further challenges by asking questions such as: *Can you produce a shape which has more spots on the inside than that one has?* and *Can you produce a shape with an odd number of spots on the perimeter?*

Suggestion(s) for support

Because the activity is differentiated by outcome it should be accessible to all pupils.

Assessment opportunities

Your own observations, as well as the children's drawings will indicate their understanding of area and their ability to produce shapes of a given area. Also listen carefully to pupils' responses during the plenary, particularly those which focus on the identification of patterns and relationships.

Opportunities for IT

The table of results used during the plenary can be produced on a spreadsheet rather than on the board. This would allow you to quickly sort the table so that the first column of numbers is in ascending order as shown above.

You could also use the spreadsheet to plot the pairs of values as (x, y) co-ordinates on a scatter-graph. This will show that there is a relationship between the spots on the perimeter and spots on the inside (the scatter-graph should show a straight line sloping downwards from left to right).

Display ideas

The children's annotated drawings can be used to create a display together with a table summarizing the numbers of spots on the perimeter and on the inside.

THE PAINTED CUBE

To identify and explain numerical patterns and relationships. To make predictions based on numerical patterns.

†† *Whole-class introduction followed by work in pairs and a whole-class plenary.*

🕐 *Introduction 10–15 minutes; main activity 20–25 minutes; plenary 15–20 minutes; total 45–60 minutes.*

Previous skills/knowledge needed

Children should be familiar with three-dimensional shapes and have some experience of investigating numerical patterns and sequences.

Key background information

This activity provides children with an opportunity to investigate number patterns and sequences in the context of three-dimensional shapes.

Pupils first explore some of the physical features of a cube and then move on to investigate numerical aspects of those features. The aim is for children to develop the ability to identify and continue numerical sequences as well as having the ability to make predictions and generalizations.

Preparation

During the main activity pupils will need to use multilink cubes. Prepare trays or small containers of multilink so that these can be handed out quickly after the introduction. Use 27 red multilink to make a 3 × 3 × 3 cube and make another one with 27 white multilink.

Place the red cube in a large container which does not have see-through sides (such as a large tin or a waste paper bin). These items will be required during the introduction.

Resources

Multilink cubes, red and white cubes (as described in 'Preparation'), large container, paper, pencils.

What to do

Introduction

Hold up the cube made from 27 white multilink and ask: *What do we call this shape?* Use this as an opportunity to discuss the features of a cube, using language such as 'faces', 'corners', 'edges', 'squares', and so on. Also, ask pupils how many multilink have been used to make the cube and how they worked out the answer.

Place the container holding the red cube on the table and tell the children to imagine that it is a tin of red paint. Explain that you are going to lower the white cube into the tin so that all of the outer faces are coated in red paint. Lower the white cube into the container and then slowly pull out the red cube. Make it clear that only the six outer faces of the cube have been coated in paint and no paint has seeped through the gaps or holes in the cubes. Tell the class that the painted cube will be left to dry and then broken up into the original 27 cubes from which it was made. Ask the children to discuss, in pairs, what these 27 individual cubes will look like.

After a few minutes invite pupils to tell you what they think, and discuss the responses. The conclusion should be that there are four types of cubes – those which have 3 red faces and 3 white faces, those which have 2 red and 4 white faces, those which have 1 red and 5 white faces and finally those which have 6 white faces. Ensure that all pupils are clear about these possibilities and are aware of the location of each one in relation to the $3 \times 3 \times 3$ cube.

Main activity

Ask pupils to work in pairs. Explain that first they must make a $3 \times 3 \times 3$ cube (not necessarily using a single colour) to use as a visual aid. Tell them to imagine that the cube is made from 27 white multilink and has been dipped into red paint as described during the introduction. The initial task is to work out how many multilink there are of each red/white colour combination discussed during the introduction.

Those who complete this task quickly can consider the situation in which a $4 \times 4 \times 4$ white cube is dipped into a tin of red paint. Again they must work out how many multilink there are of each red/white colour combination.

While pupils are working make a copy of this table on the board.

Size	3 red 3 white faces	2 red 4 white faces	1 red 5 white faces	6 white faces	Total Cubes
$2 \times 2 \times 2$					
$3 \times 3 \times 3$					
$4 \times 4 \times 4$					
$5 \times 5 \times 5$					
$6 \times 6 \times 6$					

When the majority of pupils have completed the initial task, stop the class and discuss the findings. Start by asking how many multilink will have 3 red and 3 white faces and ask the children to remind you where these are located on the original 3 × 3 × 3 cube. Repeat this for the other red/white colour combinations. Record the results in the appropriate row of the table.

Ask the children to repeat this for cubes of other sizes, starting with a 4 × 4 × 4 cube. Children can make the cube first if they wish, although some may prefer to tackle the activity without the practical apparatus.

When pupils have investigated a 4 × 4 × 4 cube tell them to consider various other sizes such as 2 × 2 × 2 or 5 × 5 × 5.

Plenary

Discuss the findings and record these on the table. Use some of the large cubes made by the pupils to explain the results, particularly for the benefit of those who did not progress on to the larger cubes. As before, ensure that pupils are aware of the locations of the various red/white combinations. The completed table should look like the one below.

Ask pupils to look at the columns of numbers and to tell you what they notice. Pose questions like: *Why are there always 8 multilink with 3 red and 3 white faces?* and

Why do the numbers in the third column go up by 12 each time? Here are explanations for each column of numbers.

3 red, 3 white These are the 8 corner cubes and all cubes have 8 corners.

2 red, 4 white These are located along the edges of the cube and all cubes have 12 edges. As the dimensions of the cube increases by 1, so does the number of cubes along each edge. There are 12 edges and so there are 12 additional cubes of this type.

1 red, 5 white These are square arrangements located in the centre of each face of the large cube. For example a 4 × 4 × 4 cube has an inner 2 by 2 square on each face (i.e. made from 4 cubes). There are six faces and so there are 6 × 4 = 24 of this type of cube.

6 white These represent a smaller inner cube which does not come into contact with the red paint because it is protected by the outer layer of multilink.

Finally, ask the children to predict the numbers of each red/white combination for cubes not shown on the table, for example a 7 × 7 × 7 or a 10 × 10 × 10.

Size	3 red 3 white faces	2 red 4 white faces	1 red 5 white faces	6 white faces	Total Cubes
2 × 2 × 2	8	0	0	0	8
3 × 3 × 3	8	12	6	1	27
4 × 4 × 4	8	24	24	8	64
5 × 5 × 5	8	36	54	27	125
6 × 6 × 6	8	48	96	64	216

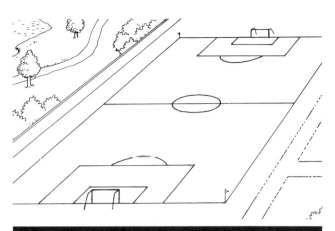

Suggestion(s) for extension

After the children have considered several different sizes of cube during the main activity they could tabulate their results and try to identify the patterns discussed above.

Suggestion(s) for support

The early stages of this activity should be accessible to all pupils, although some might benefit from adult supervision.

Assessment opportunities

Most pupils should be capable of making cubes of various sizes and using these to investigate the red/white colour combinations. Their constructions and written work will provide evidence of this. Ask those who progress quickly during the main activity to look at their results and try to spot patterns in the numbers. There may be some written evidence of this although most will present itself during the plenary discussion. It is therefore important to make a mental note of those pupils who can identify and explain the patterns and use them to make predictions.

Display ideas

Children can make three-dimensional drawings on spotted paper of the various cubes produced during the activity. These can be displayed together with a brief description of the investigation and a table summarizing the results.

FOOTBALL STRIPS

To identify simple relationships between variables. To make predictions based on simple relationships. To solve a problem in a logical, methodical way.

†† *Whole-class introduction followed by individual work and a whole-class plenary.*

⊕ *Introduction 5–10 minutes; main activity 15–20 minutes; plenary 10–15 minutes; total 30–45 minutes.*

Key background information

If children work in a logical, methodical way when investigating and solving problems they can usually progress more quickly. It is therefore important that they are encouraged to work in this way from an early age by tackling activities with a clear underlying structure or pattern which can be highlighted and discussed. The long-term aim is for pupils to be always looking for patterns to help them solve problems more efficiently. This activity is a 'how many ways?' situation which will be tackled by some pupils in a random, exhaustive way, while others will identify the underlying patterns and use them to make predictions.

Preparation

Make copies of photocopiable page 112 so that there is at least one copy per pupil.

Resources

Photocopiable page 112, coloured pencils or crayons, paper, scissors, glue, board/flip chart.

What to do

Introduction

Describe the following scenario to the class. The local football team has got shirts in two colours, red and blue, and shorts in two colours, again red and blue. Ask pupils to describe the possible football strips that a player could wear using these colours of shirts and shorts. You could record these by quickly sketching them on the board. There should be four different football strips.

Main activity

Explain to pupils that the local football team has just bought some green shirts in addition to the shirts and shorts they already have as described during the introduction. Hand out the copies of photocopiable page 112 and the coloured pencils or crayons and ask pupils to colour all of the football strips that could be worn. These can be cut out and stuck onto a sheet of paper.

When the children have completed the initial task (there should be six different football strips) set them similar problems based on other numbers of available colours. You can set individual pupils different tasks. Here are a few possibilities:

shirts in 3 colours and shorts in 2 colours
shirts in 2 colours and shorts in 2 colours
shirts in 2 colours and shorts in 3 colours
shirts in 4 colours and shorts in 2 colours
shirts in 2 colours and shorts in 4 colours   …and so on.

Pupils can choose the actual colours they use and again the strips can be cut out and stuck on paper.

While pupils are working on the main activity make a copy of this table on the board.

Shirt Colours	Shorts Colours	Possible Strips

Plenary

Start by discussing the first stage of the main activity. How many different strips can be made using shirts in three colours and shorts in two colours? Enter the appropriate numbers in the first row of the table. Also remind pupils of the situation discussed during the introduction (shirts in two colours and shorts in two colours) and enter the numbers in the second row of the table. Then invite pupils to explain their other findings from the main activity by holding up their sheets of football strips and filling in the appropriate numbers on the table. Extend the table if necessary.

Ask pupils to look carefully at the table of results. Can they see a connection between the number of colours available and the number of different strips that can be made? It is likely that some pupils will notice that the number in the final column is the product of the numbers in the two previous columns. Ask pupils to use this relationship to predict situations which are not shown in the table by asking questions such as: *How many different strips can be made using shirts in five colours and shorts in three colours?*

Finally, refer back to the situation shown in the first row of the table (shirts in three colours and shorts in two colours) but explain that now the football team has socks in two colours. Ask pupils how many different football strips can be made and to give reasons for their answers. There are 12 different football strips (3 x 2 x 2) and one possible explanation is that the six strips produced earlier can now be made twice; first using socks in one colour and then using socks in the other colour.

Suggestion(s) for extension

During the main activity some pupils might be able to spot the relationship between the colours available and the number of different strips that can be made. Ask them to write this down in their own words and then to investigate the effect of introducing socks in different colours.

Suggestion(s) for support

The nature of the activity is such that it should be accessible to all pupils.

Assessment opportunities

Observe pupils carefully during the main activity. Some children will tackle it in a random way while others will try to find the football strips in a more logical, methodical manner, for example, by keeping the colour of the shorts constant while varying the colour of the shirts. Ask pupils to explain their approach and ask those who have finished to explain how they know they have not missed out any of the strips. The pupils' responses will provide an insight into the way they are thinking and their ability to think logically and use pattern to solve problems. During the plenary, make a note of those pupils who are able to identify the relationships between the variables and are able to make predictions.

Display ideas

The colourful nature of the children's work makes it ideal for producing an eye-catching display.

Reference to photocopiable sheet

Photocopiable page 112 gives a number of football strips for the children to colour in.

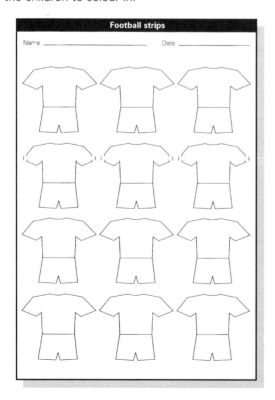

FOOTBALL LEAGUES

To identify simple relationships between variables. To make predictions based on simple relationships. To solve a problem in a logical, methodical way.

†† *Whole-class introduction followed by individual work and a whole-class plenary.*

🕐 *Introduction 5–10 minutes; main activity 25–30 minutes; plenary 15–20 minutes; total 45–60 minutes.*

Previous skills/knowledge needed

No specific previous knowledge is required although it would be useful if children have already completed the activity 'Football strips' on page 54 so that its conclusions can be compared with those reached here.

Key background information

This activity, like the previous one, requires children to investigate how many ways a particular situation can be arranged. Different pupils will tackle it in different ways with some adopting a methodical approach while others explore the possibilities in a more random fashion. Not only do the two activities use a different context but they are also different in the way they can be generalized. In the activity 'Football strips' the number of different strips was simply the product of the shirt colours and the shorts colours. In 'Football leagues' the number of matches

played can be found by first multiplying the number of teams by itself. This method, however, produces an answer which includes some matches where teams are supposedly playing against themselves, which is clearly not what happens in reality. These matches must therefore be subtracted from the answer. In 'Football strips' it is possible to wear a red shirt with red shorts but in 'Football leagues' a team cannot play against itself.

Preparation
On a large sheet of paper make a copy of the table shown at the bottom of page 58.

Resources
Paper, pencils, board/flip chart.

What to do
Introduction
Start by asking the children if they know how many Premier League football matches are played altogether during a season. It is unlikely that anyone will know the answer although some may well have a guess. Tell pupils that you do not know the answer either but by the end of the lesson everyone in the class should be able to work it out for themselves.

Tell the children that first you are going to discuss what happens in a league with only four teams in it. Ask what normally happens in a league. Discuss pupils' responses, ensuring that everyone appreciates that every team plays each of the other teams twice; once at home and once away. Write the names of four teams on the board, perhaps allowing pupils to suggest names, or alternatively use the letters A, B, C and D. Then ask the children to tell you the matches which will be played and record these on the board as a list. Like this:

A v B
B v D
D v C
B v A   ...and so on.

There is no need to record all of the possibilities at this stage since pupils are going to complete the task themselves during the main activity. Use the examples on the board to stress that teams play each other twice (A v B and B v A are both on the list above).

Main activity
The first stage is for pupils to list all of the matches which are played in a four team league (there are 12 matches). When the children think they have completed the list check it for any omissions or repeated matches.

The next stage is for pupils to list all of the matches for leagues of other sizes. Children could consider a league with three teams, or five teams, or six teams. When pupils have successfully investigated two or three different situations, ask them to look for patterns in the results which will allow them to work out quickly how many matches are played in a league with eight, nine or ten teams.

Plenary
Ask pupils to tell you the results of the main activity and record these on the board. You could use a table like this.

Teams	Matches Played
2	2
3	6
4	12
5	20
6	30

If a two team league was not considered during the main activity then you can ask pupils to quickly work out how many matches would be played and include it in the table.

Now ask the children whether they can see any patterns in the results or any quick ways of working out the number of matches. Some pupils might have noticed that the numbers in the matches column increase by 4, then by 6,

then by 8, then by 10 and so on. This pattern could be used to predict the number of matches for any given number of teams. Other children might remember the earlier work they did in the activity 'Football strips' and so use multiplication. For example, if there are four teams there are 4 × 4 = 16 matches but 4 of these must be subtracted because they represent a team playing against itself. Another way of expressing this is therefore 4 × 3 = 12. Similarly with five teams there are (5 × 5) – 5 = 20 matches or alternatively 5 × 4 = 20 matches.

There is also a visual way to explain these relationships. Start by asking: *Has anyone seen the large tables printed in newspapers or magazines which give the result of every match played during the season?* Ask pupils to describe the structure of this table. The table for a five team league is shown at the bottom of the page.

Draw the children's attention to the table you have drawn on a large sheet of paper and ask one of the pupils to explain how it is used to display all of the season's results. Write an imaginary result in one of the cells and explain what it means, for example the result shown below indicates that Team A beat Team B 2–1 when they played at Team A's ground. Ask pupils to explain why some of the cells have been shaded in. Then ask them to explain how they can quickly work out how many results will appear on the grid. This visual aid should help pupils to understand how to work out the number of matches played for leagues of any size. In general, if there are n teams in the league, there will be n × (n-1) matches.

Return to the very first question posed during the introduction (*How many Premier League football matches are played altogether during a season?*) and discuss this with the children in the light of what has been discovered during the activity.

Finally, ask pupils why the method of working out the number of possibilities in 'Football strips' is different to the method in 'Football leagues'. The number of different football strips can also be summarized in a table (see below) but the key difference is that there are no shaded cells because it is possible to have red-red, blue-blue and green-green.

		S H I R T		
		Red	Blue	Green
S H O R T S	Red			
	Blue			
	Green			

		A W A Y				
		Team A	Team B	Team C	Team D	Team E
H O M E	Team A		2-1			
	Team B					
	Team C					
	Team D					
	Team E					

Suggestion(s) for extension

Some children will progress further than others during the main activity and therefore be able to investigate the patterns and relationships which exist and start to make predictions and generalizations.

Suggestion(s) for support

The main activity should be accessible to all pupils since differentiation is by outcome.

Assessment opportunities

Observe the children carefully during the main activity to see what sorts of approaches they are adopting. Some will list the matches in a purely random way while others will be more methodical. Ask the children to explain why they are listing the matches in a particular way and, when pupils think they have a complete list, ask them how they know it is complete. Your observations, the children's responses and their written work will all provide an insight into the way they are thinking and the extent to which they are using order and pattern to explore the possibilities. Also, make a note of those pupils who, during the main activity or the plenary, are able to identify patterns in the results, make predictions and generalize the situation.

Display ideas

Display a complete list of matches for leagues of different sizes in the classroom together with an explanation of how the total number of matches can be worked out, perhaps using tables like those shown above.

INPUT-OUTPUT MACHINES

To follow accurately a set of rules involving various arithmetical operations. To use inputs and outputs to identify the rule which is being applied. To start to understand and use inverse operations.

†† *Whole-class introduction followed by a game in pairs and a whole-class plenary.*

⊕ *Introduction 15–20 minutes; main activity 20–25 minutes; plenary 10–15 minutes; total 45–60 minutes.*

Previous skills/knowledge needed

Children will need to be able to calculate mentally using a variety of operations involving one and two-digit numbers.

Key background information

Towards the end of Key Stage Two, and particularly at Key Stage Three, children will encounter a wide range of formulae in mathematics as well as in other subjects such as science. An understanding of what a formula is and how it is used can be developed using the notion of an input-output machine. A number can be fed into the machine and an output is provided. The machine does this by following a set of instructions accurately and consistently. This activity introduces pupils to input-output machines through various interactive activities which can be conducted with the whole class or in pairs.

Preparation

Make copies of photocopiable page 113 so that there is one copy for each child. During the main activity each pair of pupils will require a set of cards which illustrate different types of input-output machine. Photocopiable page 114 can be used to produce sets of cards although these do cover a wide range of ability. Photocopiable page 115 can be used to produce sets of cards matched to the ability of the pupils, for example if you are working with less able pupils you could produce a set which uses only single-digit addition and subtraction.

Resources

Photocopiable pages 113 and 114, photocopiable page 115 (optional), sets of cards as described in 'Preparation', pencils, board/flip chart.

What to do

Introduction

Stand up in front of the class and tell them that you are an input-output machine and that when a number is fed in you will use a rule to provide an output. Explain that the aim is for the children to work out what the rule is. Ask pupils to call out an input number and respond with an output (use a simple rule, for example add 3). Repeat this three or four times. Tell the children to put their hand up when they think they know what the rule is, but don't ask them to tell you just yet. Ask for another input and then invite one of the pupils who thinks they know the rule to provide the

output. This enables you to check whether or not they have worked it out correctly without letting the whole class know what the rule is. Tell the pupil whether he or she is correct or not. Invite more inputs and again allow pupils who think they know the rule to provide the outputs as a way of checking. Repeat this until the majority of pupils know what the rule is.

Tell the class that the input does not have to be a number and invite them to call out letters of the alphabet. Whatever letter is called out, respond with the letter which is three places further on in the alphabet, for example if the input is P then the output is S, and if the input is Y then the output is B (go back to the start of the alphabet). Repeat the process described above until the majority of pupils have worked out the rule.

You can also use words. Invite pupils to provide the name of a town or city and use the last letter of the input as the first letter of the output. For example, if the input is Hull the output could be Liverpool, if the input is Manchester the output could be Reading, if the input is Coventry the output could be York, and so on.

Finally, return to using numbers but this time use a rule that is more challenging, for example multiply by 3 and add 2.

Main activity

Explain to the children that you want them to play the same game but this time in pairs. Hand out the cards you have produced and explain that one person is the number machine and must pick a card to find out what sort of machine they are. The other person must provide inputs, for which the machine will provide outputs. The person providing the inputs must record all of the numbers in a

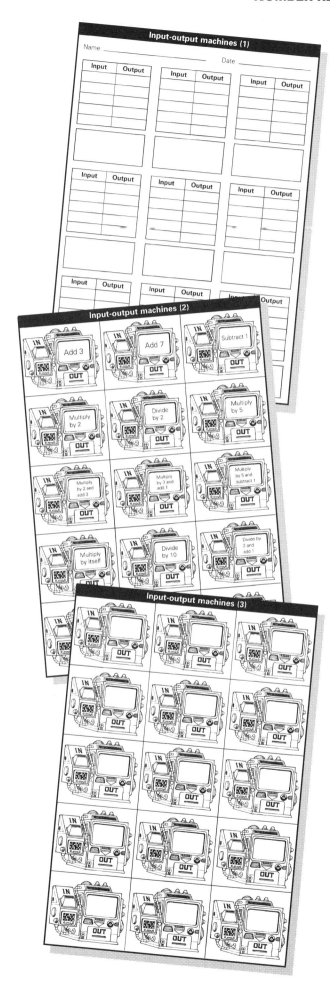

table using photocopiable page 113 and try to work out what the machine is doing. No more than five inputs are allowed. The box under the table is for recording what the machine is doing. Pupils should take turns at being the machine.

Plenary
Use the plenary to start to explore inverse operations, that is, working out inputs for given outputs. Pick a card from one of the packs the pupils have been using and show it to the class (you might like to quickly sketch it on the board). Explain to the children that you are going to provide an output from this machine and they must work out the input. Start with fairly straightforward machines (such as add 5) and gradually move on to ones involving two stages (multiply by 2 and add 3). Ask pupils to explain how they worked out the input each time and start to introduce the idea of inverses or 'doing the opposite' or 'working backwards'.

Suggestion(s) for extension
The more able pupils in the class can use sets of cards that show challenging machines involving two stages (for instance, multiply by two and then add one) or involving more complex concepts such as remainders, division, squaring, and so on.

Suggestion(s) for support
The less able pupils can use fairly straightforward machines involving a single stage.

Assessment opportunities
Your observations throughout the activity, together with the children's written work, will provide an indication of their ability to use input-output machines (when they are the machine) and also to work out the rules which are being used (when they are providing the inputs). Also, make a note of those pupils during the plenary who are beginning to understand and use inverse operations.

Display ideas
Pupils could draw their own input-output machine, perhaps as part of their art work. These could be displayed together with a table of inputs and outputs for each one. A banner at the top of the display could pose the question 'Can you work out what these machines are doing?'

Reference to photocopiable sheets
Photocopiable page 113 provides blank tables onto which the children record the numbers of their input-output machines. Photocopiable page 114 provides some examples of the type of problems you could set the children. Photocopiable page 115 provides a number of blank machines which you can use to produce your own set of cards appropriate to the ability of the pupils.

Calculations

Calculations can be carried out in many different ways. Some answers are known as facts and so can be recalled instantly, some require mental manipulation, some are best tackled using pencil and paper methods and for others a calculator is the most appropriate tool. These different approaches represent a continuum but the boundaries between them are blurred. Initially, pupils will not be able to recall addition facts, doubles and multiplication facts instantly; they will need to think and work things out in their heads. However, with much reinforcement and practice, what were once the results of mental calculations will eventually become memorized facts and these in turn will empower pupils to carry out calculations of increasing complexity using both mental and pencil and paper methods.

This chapter contains activities which focus on the learning of number facts, on mental calculations and on pencil and paper methods although the precise method which is being employed will vary from one pupil to the other. Traditionally there has been a heavy emphasis on the development, reinforcement and practise of standard pencil and paper routines at the expense of mental methods. However, it is important to ensure that mental methods are always seen as a first resort and therefore given appropriate emphasis. This is reflected in the balance of activities in this section. The activities are also intended to complement those featured in published schemes and so there is a heavy emphasis on problem-solving, open-ended and investigative work.

Many of the activities in chapter two also require pupils to carry out calculations of various kinds and so could be used to reinforce and develop these skills. However, in chapter two the main focus is on special numbers, patterns and relationships rather than the calculations themselves. You will therefore need to consider carefully the appropriateness of the activities in meeting your learning objectives.

PENTOMINOES ON A 100-SQUARE

To add whole numbers up to 100 without a calculator. To use the number patterns in a 100-square to solve problems.

†† *Whole-class introduction followed by individual work and a whole-class plenary.*

⏱ *Introduction 10–15 minutes; main activity 25–30 minutes; plenary 10–15 minutes; total 45–60 minutes.*

Previous skills/knowledge needed

It would be helpful if children have already encountered pentominoes and know what they are, perhaps as part of their shape and space work. A pentomino is formed by shading in five connected squares on squared paper. The squares must be connected along an edge, not just at a corner as shown by the examples below.

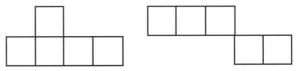

This is a pentomino.   This is not a pentomino.

Children could investigate how many different pentominoes there are, possibly using multilink cubes to represent the squares. The task would therefore be to make as many different shapes as possible by clipping together five multilink cubes but all five cubes must be in contact with the table (and obviously connected along an edge). This activity raises the question of what we mean by 'different' and the distinction between different shape and different position. For example, these three pentominoes are all the same shape but are in different positions.

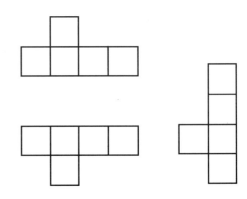

There are twelve different pentominoes as shown opposite.

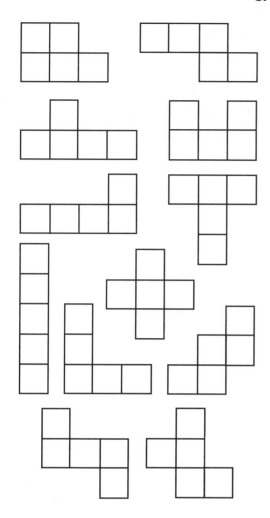

Key background information

This activity gives children an opportunity to practise and apply their addition skills involving whole numbers up to 100. It is a more interesting and more challenging alternative to doing pages of 'sums'. Rather than focusing solely on the arithmetic, the activity also encourages children to investigate and make use of the number patterns that exist in a 100-square.

Preparation

Make copies of photocopiable page 116 so that there is one for each child. During the main activity children will need a 100-square in which each square is 2cm × 2cm so that it can be used in conjunction with multilink cubes. Children can produce their own 100-square at the start of the activity using sheets of 2cm squared paper or, alternatively, you can enlarge the 100-square on photocopiable page 104 to the required size. Produce one of these 100-squares for yourself, to use during the introduction and plenary.

Resources

Photocopiable page 116, 2cm squared paper (or enlarged copies of photocopiable page 104 as described in 'Preparation'), multilink cubes (five per pupil), lined or squared paper, pencils, board/flip chart.

What to do
Introduction

If children are familiar with pentominoes then recap earlier work on them by asking a question such as: *Can anyone remember what a pentomino is?* Alternatively draw two or three pentominoes on the board and ask: *What do we call these shapes?* Discuss the key features of a pentomino, that is, they are made from five squares connected along their edges. You can also demonstrate pentominoes by clipping together five multilink cubes, stressing that all five must be able to lie in contact with the table.

If the children have not encountered pentominoes before then you will need to spend more time explaining what they are and discussing them. When you feel the children understand, ask them to come out and draw examples of pentominoes on the board.

Hold up the 100-square you prepared earlier and ask pupils to tell you what it is. Also ask them what they notice about the size of the squares (hold up a multilink cube or a multilink pentomino as a clue). Use a multilink pentomino to demonstrate how five numbers on the 100-square can be covered. Place the pentomino in the top-left corner of the 100-square (where the lowest numbers are) and ask the children to work out the sum of the five numbers. Rotate the pentomino or flip it over and again ask pupils to work out the sum of the five numbers.

Main activity

If you have not used photocopiable page 104 to produce the enlarged 100-squares then hand out the squared paper and explain to the children that you first want them to make a 100-square of their own using 2cm squared paper. When they have done this, give out the multilink cubes and the copies of photocopiable page 116. Tell the children to make a pentomino using the multilink and then to answer the questions on the photocopiable sheet. Pupils can record their answers on lined or squared paper.

Plenary

Start by discussing the effects of moving a pentomino right, left, up or down one square. When a pentomino is moved one square to the right the total increases by 5 since each cube will be covering a number one more than it was previously. When a pentomino is moved down one square the total increases by 50 since each cube is covering a number 10 more than it was previously. Ask the children to explain why the total increases or decreases by 5 or by 50. Did the children use this information to help them when they were finding pentominoes with a total of 100 or 200? If any children say that they did then ask them to explain how.

Discuss the answers to questions 5 to 8, each time asking the children to explain how they went about finding their solutions in terms of both the problem-solving strategies used as well as the methods of calculation. Ask children to come out and draw their pentominoes on the board and write the total at the side.

Suggestion(s) for extension

Those children who complete the questions on photocopiable page 116 could try to find additional solutions to questions 7 and 8. If any children require a further challenge then ask them to investigate this question: Is it possible to make pentominoes that have every total between the smallest (15) and the highest (490) or are there some totals which are impossible to make?

Suggestion(s) for support

Questions 7 and 8 can be adapted to match the ability of certain individuals, for example children could try to find a pentomino with a total of 20 or 30. You might also want to include arrows in questions 1 and 2 to indicate movement right and left.

Assessment opportunities

The children's written work will provide evidence of their ability to add whole numbers up to 100 without a calculator. Also observe children carefully during the main activity and, if necessary, ask them to explain how they are adding the five numbers, particularly in the case of those who are relying on mental methods.

Display ideas

Children can copy their solutions to questions 7 and 8 onto 2cm squared paper, cut them out and use these to form a display under appropriate headings such as 'These pentominoes have a total of 100' or 'These pentominoes have a total of 200'. The question posed in the 'Suggestion(s) for extension' section could also be used as the basis of an on-going display, challenging pupils to find pentominoes which have all of the totals between 15 (the smallest) and 490 (the highest). They could add pentominoes with new totals to the display as they find them.

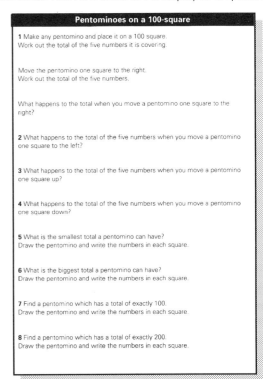

Reference to photocopiable sheet

Photocopiable page 116 provides a number of questions that the children have to answer with regard to the pentominoes they have created out of multilink. The answers to the sheet are given below.

1 When you move a pentomino one square to the right its total increases by 5.

2 When you move a pentomino one square to the left its total decreases by 5.

3 When you move a pentomino one square up its total decreases by 50.

4 When you move a pentomino one square down its total increases by 50.

5 The smallest pentomino total is 15.

1	2	3	4	5

6 The biggest pentomino total is 490.

96	97	98	99	100

7 These pentominoes have totals of 100.

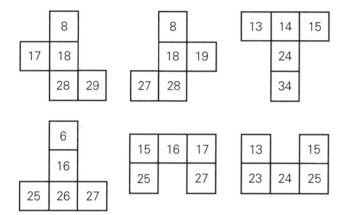

8 These pentominoes have totals of 200.

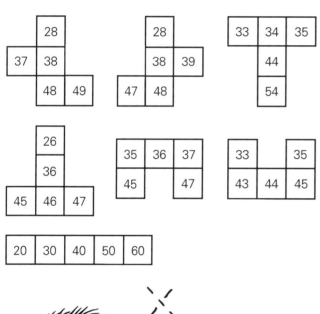

THE WALL

To add one and two-digit numbers without a calculator. To identify relationships and make general statements.

†† *Whole-class introduction followed by individual work and a whole-class plenary.*

🕐 *Introduction 10–15 minutes; main activity 25–30 minutes; plenary 10–15 minutes; total 45–60 minutes.*

Key background information

This activity provides children with another opportunity to practise their non-calculator arithmetic skills in a problem-solving situation. It is important that basic number skills are developed in these sorts of contexts rather than in isolation otherwise children will not only become bored but will also fail to see that mathematics can be used and applied in many different ways.

Preparation

Make copies of photocopiable page 117 so that there are at least two copies per pupil. If you are concerned about photocopying costs then the sheet can be reduced to A5 size so that there are two copies on each A4 sheet. Alternatively, give each pupil one copy of the sheet and tell them that subsequent arrangements of bricks must be drawn on plain paper.

Also, make a copy of this arrangement of bricks on the board.

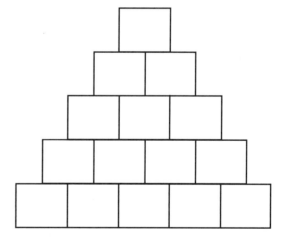

Resources

Photocopiable page 117, plain paper, pencils, board/flip chart.

What to do

Introduction

Invite pupils to provide you with five different single-digit numbers and write these into the five bricks in the bottom row of the arrangement on the board so that it looks something like the following arrangement:

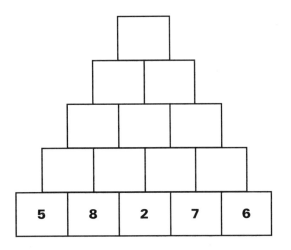

Tell the children that you are going to use a rule to calculate the numbers in the second row and they must try to work out the rule you are using. Calculate each number by adding the two numbers immediately below. The example above would look like this:

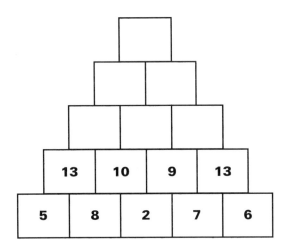

Ask the children to put up their hands when they think they know what the rule is. Provide clues if necessary by saying, for example: *Why did I write 13 in this brick?* and *Look at the two bricks underneath the 13.* Ask three pupils who have worked out the rule to each come and write a number into the third row. Repeat this until the wall is complete. The completed example would look like this:

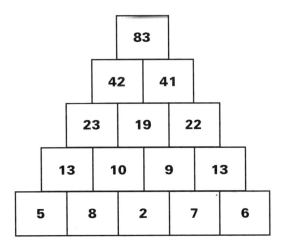

Ask a pupil to explain the rule to the rest of the class.

Repeat the activity using the same rule and the same five starting numbers but this time write them in a different order across the bottom row. This should ensure that all the children understand how to complete the wall and also illustrates that changing the order produces a different number in the top brick.

Main activity

Give each child a copy of photocopiable page 117 and explain to pupils that they will be filling in the 'walls' on the sheet. However, they can only use the numbers 1 to 5 in the bottom row of bricks. Each number must be used only once (so they cannot write 5, 5, 5, 5, 5 in the bottom row) but they can be arranged in any order. Explain that the objective is for the children to try to get the biggest possible number in the top brick.

When the children think they have found the biggest number, check their work. It should look like this, although the 3 and 4 can be swapped, as can the 1 and 2.

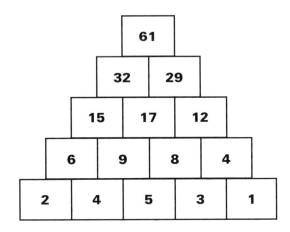

If pupils have not actually found the biggest answer then tell them to keep trying and if anyone has got an answer bigger than 61 then tell them to check their additions. Those children who find the biggest number can move on to the next task which is to find the smallest possible number in the top brick. The answer is 35 as shown below (again, the 2 and 3 can be swapped, as can the 4 and 5).

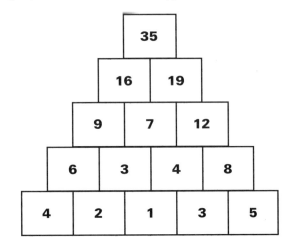

The third task is to find the biggest possible number in the top brick using any five different single-digit numbers in the bottom row. Finally, ask pupils to find the lowest possible number in the top brick using any five different single-digit numbers, including zero, in the bottom row. The solutions to these two problems are shown below.

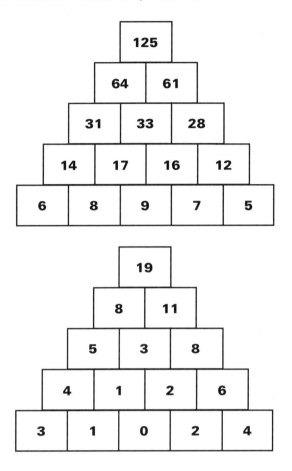

Plenary

Rub out the numbers from your arrangement of bricks on the board so that it can be used to display the children's findings. Invite a child to come out and write the numbers 1 to 5 in the bottom row of bricks to give the biggest number at the top. Ask other children to work out the subsequent rows of numbers. The number in the top brick should be 61. Tell the children to look closely at the way the numbers 1 to 5 are arranged in the bottom row and ask them what they notice. Provide prompts if necessary by saying, for example: *Where is the biggest number? Where are the smallest numbers?*

Move on to the situation in which any five different single-digit numbers in the bottom row can be used. Ask pupils to tell you the biggest number they managed to get in the top brick. If someone has made the maximum (125) ask him or her to come out and write the numbers in the bottom row of bricks and ask other pupils to work out the subsequent rows. Again, ask pupils about the way the numbers in the bottom row are arranged (9 should be in the middle, 8 and 7 either side of the 9, and 6 and 5 at the ends of the row).

Repeat these discussions for the smallest number in the top brick using 1 to 5 and also using any five different single-digit numbers, including zero. The key point to draw out is that the lowest number must be placed in the middle of the bottom row and the biggest numbers at the ends of the row.

Suggestion(s) for extension

Here are three additional challenges which can be set for those children who complete the tasks described above and require extension work.

▲ Instead of adding the two numbers in the bricks below, work out the difference. What is the biggest number you can get in the top brick using the numbers 1 to 5 in the bottom row?
The answer is 3. One possible solution is to put 5, 1, 2, 3 and 4 in the bottom row.

▲ Use the same addition rule as in the main activity. Use any five different whole numbers to get 10 in the top brick. This can only be solved by using negative numbers. There are many solutions but one possibility is to put 5, – 1, 0, 2 and 1 in the bottom row.

▲ Use the same addition rule as in the main activity. Use any five different positive numbers to get 10 in the top brick.
This can only be solved by using decimals or fractions. There are many solutions but one possibility is to put 1.5, 0.5, 0, 1 and 2.5 in the bottom row.

Suggestion(s) for support

The nature of the main activity is such that it should be accessible to all pupils.

Assessment opportunities

The children's written work will provide evidence of their ability to add one and two-digit numbers without a calculator. When the children think they have found the biggest or smallest number in the top brick, ask them what they notice about the way the numbers in the bottom row are arranged. Some children may be able to explain and make general statements regarding the connection between the position of the numbers in the bottom row and the size of the number in the top brick.

Opportunities for IT

This activity can be carried out on a spreadsheet set up in advance for pupils to use. All calculations will be carried out by the computer and so the focus for pupils will be on the identification of relationships and the making of general statements.

Enter formulae into cells on the spreadsheet as indicated on the next page. The results of the formulae (initially zero) rather than the formulae themselves will be displayed in the cells. Pupils can now type numbers, for example the numbers 1 to 5, into the first five cells of the fifth row. The numbers in the cells above will change to display the same results as in the main activity described above. The numbers in the fifth row can be changed easily, thus allowing pupils to investigate the effect this has on the top brick.

	A	B	C	D	E
1	=A2+B2				
2	=A3+B3	=B3+C3			
3	=A4+B4	=B4+C4	=C4+D4		
4	=A5+B5	=B5+C5	=C5+D5	=D5+E5	
5					
6					

Display ideas

The children's completed arrangements of bricks can be displayed under appropriate headings corresponding to the various tasks described above.

Reference to photocopiable sheet

Photocopiable page 117 provides a number of blank 'walls'. Using single digits, the children have to fill in the bricks in the wall according to various criteria.

MULTIPLICATION SQUARES

To know and use multiplication facts up to 10 × 10.

†† *Whole-class introduction followed by individual work and a whole-class plenary.*

🕐 *Introduction 10–15 minutes; main activity 20–25 minutes; plenary 15–20 minutes; total 45–60 minutes.*

Previous skills/knowledge needed

It is assumed that children will already have some knowledge of multiplication facts up to 10 × 10.

Key background information

It is essential that children know their multiplication facts, as these, together with addition facts, form the basis of mental agility with number. Children who are not able to recall multiplication facts quickly will be at a disadvantage both when learning more mathematics and also in their everyday lives. A great deal of time, therefore, needs to be spent reinforcing, practising and applying these facts.

Preparation

Make copies of photocopiable page 118 so that there is one per pupil. Depending on the approach you choose to adopt during the introduction you might need to prepare some pieces of card with multiplication problems written on them (see the 'Introduction' section opposite).

Resources

Photocopiable page 118, paper, pencils, multiplication flash-cards (optional), board/flip chart.

What to do

Introduction

Start with some quick-fire mental practice involving multiplication facts. For example, hold up a piece of card showing a multiplication such as '7 × 8' and ask the children to provide the answer. Alternatively, you could simply call out the multiplications. Try to match the questions to the abilities of the pupils and do not rely only on those who put up their hands. You could also reverse the process, so that you call out a number (say, 45) and the pupils must provide a multiplication which gives that answer. Ask for all of the possible multiplications, for example, 45 can be made in three different ways (1 × 45, 3 × 15 and 5 × 9). You might also want to reinforce the commutative property of multiplication, that is, 5 × 9 gives the same answer as 9 × 5.

Quickly draw this grid on the board.

X	3	8
2		
5		

Point to the space under the 3 and to the right of the 2 and say: *Can anyone tell me what number goes in here?* Write in the answer (6) and ask the child who gave you the answer to explain why it is 6. Repeat this with the remaining three spaces on the grid, ensuring that all the children appreciate how the multiplication square works and how the answers are achieved.

Now draw this multiplication square on the board and ask the children to explain what is different about it.

X		
	15	35
	18	42

Point to the 15 and ask the class which times-tables it appears in. Then point to the 35 and ask the same question. Now point to the space to the left of the 15 and ask the children what number must therefore be written here. Complete the multiplication grid by asking similar questions.

Main activity

Give out copies of photocopiable page 118 and ask the children to complete the multiplication squares.

When they have completed the task, ask them to make up some multiplication squares of their own, similar to the ones on the sheet. These can be passed on to other pupils to complete.

Plenary

Ask a child to come out and quickly draw a multiplication square on the board which he or she has made up themself. Ask other pupils to provide the missing numbers. Repeat this for other multiplication squares, including ones where the answers have been provided and the numbers being multiplied have to be filled in.

Finally, discuss the different ways in which the final multiplication square on the photocopiable sheet can be completed. Ask the children to call out their solutions and record these on the board. (See 'Reference to photocopiable sheet' on the next page for possible solutions as to how it could be completed.)

Suggestion(s) for extension

The main activity described above should provide sufficient challenge for most pupils, particularly the second stage in which pupils make up their own multiplication squares for others to complete. However, additional sheets, similar to photocopiable page 118, can easily be produced as an extension for some children. These could involve the multiplication of bigger numbers arranged on 3 × 3 and 4 × 4 grids.

Suggestion(s) for support
The first half of the photocopiable sheet should be accessible to all children. Similar sheets, pitched at about the same level, can easily be produced to provide additional practice for some pupils before they move on to the second half of photocopiable page 118.

Assessment opportunities
Make a note of how well pupils perform during the quick-fire mental practice. Also observe the speed at which they work during the main activity. This will indicate their knowledge of multiplication facts. Fire additional multiplication questions at individual pupils as you walk around during the main activity to keep them on their toes.

Reference to photocopiable sheet
Photocopiable page 118 provides a number of partially completed multiplication grids that the children have to complete. Completing the multiplication squares on the photocopiable sheet should be fairly straightforward and so the answers are not provided here. However, here are two possible solutions to the final question on the sheet.

X	1	2
24	24	48
12	12	24

X	3	4
8	24	32
6	18	24

These solutions make use of all of the factors of 12 (1, 2, 3, 4, 6, 8, 12 and 24) but these can be mixed in many ways to produce other solutions such as those shown below.

X	4	6
6	24	36
4	16	24

X	3	12
8	24	96
2	6	24

THE CARDIOID
To practise mental doubling strategies involving numbers up to 100. To use a pencil and ruler to draw straight lines.
†† *Whole-class introduction followed by individual work and whole-class plenary.*
⏰ *Introduction 10–15 minutes; main activity 30–35 minutes; plenary 5–10 minutes; total 45–60 minutes.*

Previous skills/knowledge needed
It is assumed that children will have already done some work on doubling and are familiar with numbers up to 100. Pupils will also need to be able to use a pencil and ruler to draw straight lines.

Key background information
With practice pupils will be able to recall instantly the doubles of single-digit numbers but in the case of larger

numbers they will usually need to calculate mentally. However, it must not be assumed that all pupils will naturally develop effective mental strategies of their own and so it is important that opportunities are provided for pupils to discuss, demonstrate and use various approaches. The activity described here focuses on these important number skills but also covers aspects of shape and space. The shape produced during the main activity is called a cardioid (meaning 'heart-shaped').

Preparation
Make copies of photocopiable page 119 so that there is one per pupil. Make a few spare copies for those children who progress to the extension activity. Also make an enlarged copy, as large as possible, to aid your explanation of the main activity.

Resources
Photocopiable page 119, pencils, rulers, board/flip chart.

What to do
Introduction
Start with a few minutes of quick-fire mental recall practice involving doubles of numbers no bigger than 20. Then write a larger number on the board, for example 23, and ask the children to double it. Ask pupils to explain how they worked it out. It is likely that the mental methods will be based on doubling 20, doubling 3 and adding the two answers. If some children suggest alternative methods, discuss these and stress that there is often more than one way of tackling a calculation and there is no single correct way (although, depending on the numbers involved, one method may be more efficient than another). Write further examples on the board for pupils to work out mentally and again ask

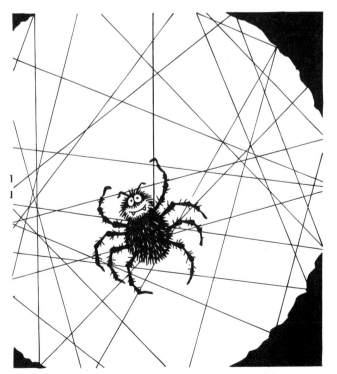

them to explain their mental methods after they have given you the answer.

Main activity
Use your enlarged copy of photocopiable page 119 to demonstrate to the children what they must do. Explain that each number must be joined to its double with a straight line using a ruler and pencil. For example 1 is joined to 2, 2 is joined to 4, 3 is joined to 6, and so on. Tell pupils that the last line they will draw will connect 35 to its double (ask them what the double is). Hand out copies of photocopiable page 119 and set the children to work.

Plenary
Start with some more quick-fire mental practice involving doubles of numbers up to 35 to reinforce what has been covered during the introduction and main activity. Then discuss the shape that has been produced on the photocopiable sheet. Ask the children to describe it in their own words. You could recap or introduce the idea of a mirror-line or line of symmetry. Provide prompts if necessary, for example you could run your finger along the line of symmetry and ask: *What do we call this line?* or *What do you notice about the pattern either side of this line.* Also introduce pupils to the word cardioid and explain what it means ('heart-shaped').

Suggestion(s) for extension
Children who require extension work could repeat the main activity but this time join each of the numbers 1 to 35 to its treble. They will first have to add another ring of numbers to the circle. The two existing rings are numbered 1 to 36 and 37 to 72. The third ring should be numbered 73 to 108.

Suggestion(s) for support
Less able children may benefit from additional support from an adult who can give them extra assistance with regard to both the doubling and the drawing.

Assessment opportunities
The main focus of this activity is on mental methods so make a note of how individual pupils perform during the quick-fire practice parts of the lesson. Also, observe children while they are working out doubles during the main activity and ask them to tell you their answers and explain their methods.

Opportunities for IT
The programs *Circle* and *Rose* produced by MicroSMILE explore similar themes to the one in this activity. Both involve joining points on a circle with straight lines although not work on doubling or trebling. The programs are available for BBC, RM Nimbus PC-186, Archimedes and Windows-based computers.

Display ideas
The visual nature of the completed work, particularly if it is coloured in, means that it can be used to produce an attractive display.

Reference to photocopiable sheet
Photocopiable page 119 shows a circle with the numbers 1 to 72. The children have to join each number to its double. The diagrams below show the patterns produced by doubling and trebling the numbers 1 to 35.

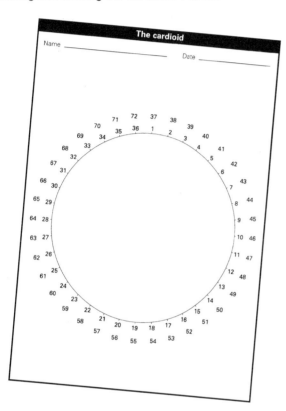

MAXIMIZE THE PRODUCT
To multiply two or more numbers without a calculator. To use findings to make predictions and generalizations.

†† *Whole-class introduction followed by individual work and a whole-class plenary.*

🕐 *Introduction 5–10 minutes; main activity 25–30 minutes; plenary 15–20 minutes; total 45–60 minutes.*

Previous skills/knowledge needed
Pupils will need to be familiar with multiplication involving whole numbers without the aid of a calculator.

Key background information
This activity provides pupils with an opportunity to practise mental multiplication skills and to apply these skills in an investigative situation. Both aspects are equally important since one of the reasons for learning arithmetic is to use it as a tool to explore new areas of mathematics.

Preparation
Clip together 15 multilink cubes in a line to form a tower.

Resources
Multilink cubes, paper, pencils, board/flip chart.

What to do
Introduction
Use the first few minutes for quick-fire mental practice involving the multiplication of whole numbers. Start with single-digit numbers and then move on to multiplying a

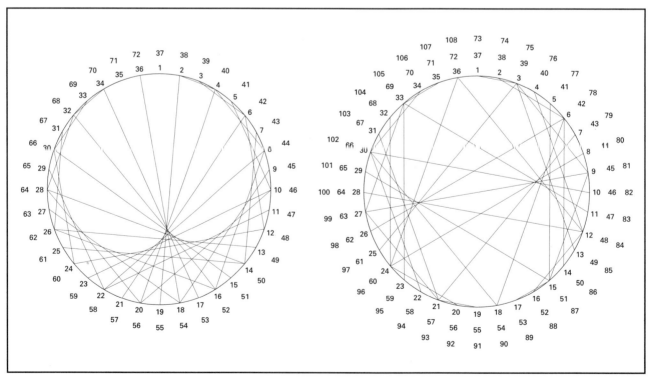

single-digit number by a two digit number up to 20. Ask pupils to explain their methods and make them aware of alternatives, for example multiplying by four or eight can be achieved by repeated doubling, while multiplying by nine can be done by multiplying by ten and then subtracting. You might also like to revise or introduce the expression 'product'.

Move on to the multiplication of three single-digit numbers, for example $4 \times 2 \times 5$. Again, ask the children to explain their methods and ensure that your discussions focus on the associative property of repeated multiplication, that is, it does not matter in which order the numbers are multiplied. For example, in the case of $4 \times 2 \times 5$ many pupils may choose to work out 2×5 first and then multiply the answer by 4.

Main activity

Hold up the multilink tower and tell the children that you are going to break it into two pieces. Ask pupils to suggest a possible way of doing this, for example, 10 and 5 or 9 and 6. Then break the tower into the two pieces suggested and record it on the board (avoid using 7 and 8). Write the two numbers, for example 5 and 10, side by side with a space between them. Then tell pupils that you are going to multiply the two numbers to get the product. Write a multiplication sign between the two numbers and complete the arithmetic with an equals sign and the answer. Clip the multilink back together and repeat the process, again recording the numbers and their product on the board.

Tell the children that you want them to find the maximum product when a strip of 15 multilink is broken into two pieces as you have just demonstrated. When they are sure that they have found the maximum product, they must investigate what happens if the strip of 15 multilink is broken into three pieces. Ask pupils to suggest a possible way of doing this and work out the product by way of example (avoid using 5, 5 and 5). Tell pupils to record their calculations clearly on paper and give out multilink cubes for them to use.

When the children have found the maximum product for two pieces ($7 \times 8 = 56$) and for three pieces ($5 \times 5 \times 5 = 125$) ask them to investigate the maximum product when the same strip of multilink is broken into four pieces, then five pieces, then six pieces, and so on.

Plenary

Invite the children to explain their findings and tabulate the maximum products on the board like this.

2 pieces	7×8	$= 56$
3 pieces	$5 \times 5 \times 5$	$= 125$
4 pieces	$3 \times 4 \times 4 \times 4$	$= 192$
5 pieces	$3 \times 3 \times 3 \times 3 \times 3$	$= 243$
6 pieces	$2 \times 2 \times 2 \times 3 \times 3 \times 3$	$= 216$

Continue the table so that all the numbers of pieces investigated by the children are recorded on the board. When you have recorded the first three lines of results, stop and ask the children if they think the maximum products will continue to increase as the number of pieces is increased. Provide a hint by saying: *What will happen if we break it into fifteen pieces?* Discuss the fact that multiplying by 1 has no effect. Continue to record the results to show that the maximum product reaches a peak of 243 when the strip of multilink is broken into five pieces.

Now say to the children: *What do you notice about the way the strip of multilink has to be broken up to get the maximum product?* Provide a visual prompt by breaking a strip of 15 multilink into the two pieces which produce the maximum product and stand them side by side. Repeat this for three pieces and four pieces to produce arrangements as shown below.

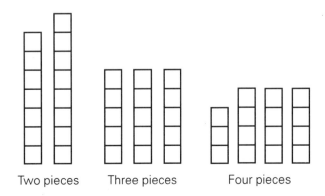

Two pieces   Three pieces   Four pieces

If necessary say: *What do you notice about the heights of the towers in each set of pieces?* Hopefully, pupils will be able to explain that the maximum product is produced when the numbers are as equal to one another as is possible or, in other words, the heights of the towers in each set have to be as equal as possible. Work through the table of results on the board to show that this is true for all of the sets of numbers.

Then say to pupils: *Suppose you were allowed to cut the strip with a knife so that the numbers of multilink in each piece were not necessarily whole numbers. Do you think that with two pieces you could get a bigger product than 56?* Ask pupils to explain their answers and use a calculator to check their prediction (the maximum product is 56.25, produced by two identical pieces, each of length 7.5). Repeat this question and discussion for three pieces, four pieces, five pieces, and so on.

Suggestion(s) for extension

If the children have successfully investigated five, six and seven pieces, ask them to consider the final question posed in the plenary section above, that is, what happens if we do not restrict the numbers in each piece to whole numbers?

Suggestion(s) for support

The nature of the activity is such that it should be accessible to all pupils since differentiation is by outcome.

Assessment opportunities

The children's written work will provide evidence of their ability to multiply two or more numbers without a calculator but also remember to ask them to explain their mental methods. When pupils have found the maximum product for two, three, four and five pieces, ask them what they notice about the numbers that give the maximum each time. If they are able to provide a correct explanation (such as the numbers are as equal as possible) then ask them to use this to predict how to get the maximum product for six or seven pieces. Pupils' responses will indicate their ability to make predictions and generalizations based on their findings.

Display ideas

The children could make drawings of their findings and these could be grouped and displayed under appropriate headings, for example 'These give the maximum product for two pieces' and 'These give the maximum product for three pieces'.

ESTIMATING DECIMAL MULTIPLIERS

To develop an understanding of place value in the context of decimals. To use trial and improvement methods. To appreciate that multiplication does not always make numbers bigger.

†† *Whole-class introduction followed by a game in pairs and a whole-class plenary.*

🕐 *Introduction 10–15 minutes; main activity 25–30 minutes; plenary 10–15 minutes; total 45–60 minutes.*

Previous skills/knowledge needed

Children should have an understanding of multiplication and be able to round decimals to the nearest whole number.

Key background information

Children are often reluctant to make estimates because they are frightened of not getting the right answer. It is therefore important that pupils are encouraged to make estimates in a wide variety of contexts and are provided with opportunities to practise the necessary skills. This activity provides such an opportunity and also allows pupils to develop their understanding of place value in the context of decimals.

Preparation

Make copies of photocopiable page 120 so that there is one for each pair. Each pair will also require two counters and a calculator. Make copies of photocopiable page 121 for those children carrying out the support activity. You will need to fill in appropriate numbers for them to use. See 'Suggestion(s) for support' below.

Resources
Photocopiable page 120, counters, calculators, pencils, paper. For the support activity – photocopiable page 121.

What to do
Introduction
Write the numbers 7 and 16 on the board as shown below.

Ask pupils to estimate what 7 would have to be multiplied by to get 16. Provide additional prompts by asking: *What is 7 multiplied by 2? What is 7 multiplied by 3?* and finally *So what do you think we should multiply by?* Write down one of the estimates (for instance 2.2) on the board as shown below.

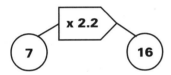

Ask the pupil who provided the answer why he or she chose that particular multiplier. Give a calculator to one of the pupils and ask him or her to check (for example, if the estimate is 2.2 then the pupil works out 7 x 2.2 = 15.4). Ask pupils to round the answer (15.4) to the nearest whole number. (It might be necessary to remind pupils how to round to the nearest whole number, possibly using a number line on the classroom wall.) Ask pupils what this means about the multiplier. *Is it too big? Is it too small? What might a better estimate be?* Rub out the first multiplier on the board and replace it with a new one (for example 2.3). Again, ask one of the pupils to check with a calculator and then round the answer to the nearest whole number. The rounded answer is 16 and so the estimate is good enough.

Now write the number 9 on the board as shown below.

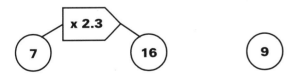

Ask the children to estimate what they would have to multiply 16 by to get 9. It is likely that some pupils will provide estimates greater than 1. Pick up on wrong answers such as these and demonstrate why they are wrong, possibly with the aid of a calculator. Ensure that all

pupils appreciate that the multiplier must be less than 1. Repeat the process described above using one of the pupils' estimates. Keep going until the estimate is good enough (in other words, when the calculator display rounded to the nearest whole number is 9).

If necessary, work through additional examples, similar to those above.

Main activity
Organize the children into pairs and give each pair a copy of photocopiable page 120, two counters and one calculator. Explain that the children must work their way along the number track, one player from School to Home and the other from Home to School. Player one places her counter on Home (number 6) and player two places his counter on School (number 8). The calculator must not be used by either player unless they are checking an estimate as part of their turn.

Player one starts by saying what she thinks the multiplier is to get from 6 to 13. Then she checks with the calculator. If the estimate is good enough (the calculator display is 13 to the nearest whole number) then she moves her counter on to 13. If the estimate is not good enough then she must wait until it is her turn again.

Then it is player two's turn. He must say what the multiplier is to get from 8 to 11, check with the calculator and move on if appropriate. The winner is the first person to complete the number track. Tell pupils to record their multipliers on paper, perhaps in the same way that you recorded them on the board during the introduction.

When pupils have completed the game they can repeat it working in the opposite direction.

Plenary

Ask pupils to explain how they decided what their first estimate would be. Did they just guess or did they think about it more carefully? You could also work through one or two additional examples, similar to those in the introduction, but this time requiring greater accuracy as described in the extension section below.

Suggestion(s) for extension

Tell able pupils to round the calculator display to one decimal place rather than to the nearest whole number. If this gives the required number then the estimate is good enough. For example, imagine player one estimates that the multiplier is 2.1 to get from 6 to 13. Checking with a calculator this gives 6 x 2.1 = 12.6 (too low). Next turn they try 2.2 which gives 13.2 (too high). Next turn they try 2.15 to give 12.9 (too low). Next turn they try 2.16 to give 12.96 which is 13.0 to one decimal place and so the estimate is good enough.

Suggestion(s) for support

Weaker pupils could use a track comprising numbers which are always increasing, that is, the multiplier is always greater than one. This sort of track would only be able to be used in one direction and so pupils would have to share a track and both move in the same direction or have one track each. Photocopiable page 121 provides a blank track onto which you can enter numbers suitable for the ability of the pupils.

Assessment opportunities

The children's responses during the introduction and plenary will give an indication of their understanding of decimals and place value. Also observe pupils carefully when they are playing the game and be prepared to intervene, asking them to explain why they chose a particular estimate.

Opportunities for IT

A spreadsheet can be set up in advance for pupils to use to practise estimating decimal multipliers. Type column headings into the first row of the spreadsheet as shown below. Then enter the formulae =A2*B2 into cell D2 and copy this into the cells below as far as row 11. Note that

an asterisk is used to denote multiplication. The results of the formulae (initially zero) rather than the formulae themselves will be displayed in the cells. Starting numbers can be entered into column A and target numbers into column C. Pupils must estimate the multiplier required to get from the starting number to the target and enter this estimate in column B. The answer produced by their multiplier is displayed in column D and so can be compared with the target they are aiming for. Pupils can adjust their multiplier until their answer is sufficiently accurate.

Reference to photocopiable sheets

Working in pairs the children have to move their counters along the number track on photocopiable page 120 estimating appropriate multipliers to get from one number to the next. Photocopiable page 121 is provided for those children who need extra support. The spaces have been left blank so that you can fill in numbers appropriate to their ability.

	A	B	C	D	E
1	Start No.	My Multiplier	Target	My Answer	
2	7		24	= A2 * B2	
3	23		35	= A3 * B3	
4	11		50	= A4 * B4	
5	29		36	= A5 * B5	
6	17		12	= A6 * B6	

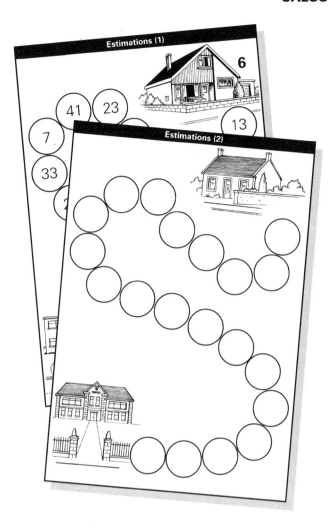

Resources
Paper, pencils.

What to do
Introduction

Start by discussing the concept of halving and possible mental strategies for halving. Ask pupils: *What does half mean?* and *How do you halve a number?* and discuss their responses. The key point to draw out is that halving involves division into two equal pieces. Then ask the children to halve specific numbers, starting with fairly straightforward numbers (numbers up to 20) and gradually moving on to more challenging ones (up to 100). Ask pupils to explain the methods they use when halving bigger numbers and discuss these with the whole class. The most common strategies are likely to involve halving the tens and then halving the units.

Main activity

Ask the children to provide you with a number between, say, 20 and 30. (It does not have to be an even number.) Write the number in the head segment of the centipede you drew on the board earlier. Then write a number in the second segment using these rules:
▲ If the previous number is even then halve it.
▲ If the previous number is odd then add 1.
Do not tell pupils the rules at this stage, instead ask them to tell you what you have done to get the second number (you will have either halved the first number or added 1). Write in the next number using the same rules and again ask the children to tell you what you have done. Repeat this until you get the answer 1 (you may have to quickly draw additional body segments to accommodate the numbers).

Here is a complete centipede using 27 as the starting number.

NUMBER CENTIPEDES

To halve even numbers without a calculator.

†† *Whole-class introduction followed by individual work and a whole-class plenary.*

⊕ *Introduction 5–10 minutes; main activity 30–35 minutes; plenary 10–15 minutes; total 45–60 minutes.*

Previous skills/knowledge needed
Pupils will need to be able to identify odd and even numbers and be familiar with the idea of halving.

Key background information
This activity provides children with an opportunity to practise mental methods for halving. This can be done by simply giving pupils a list of numbers to halve but the alternative approach presented here requires children to use their knowledge and skills in an open-ended problem-solving situation. This is more likely to motivate pupils than routine exercises.

Preparation
Draw on the board a centipede with six or seven body segments like the one shown top right.

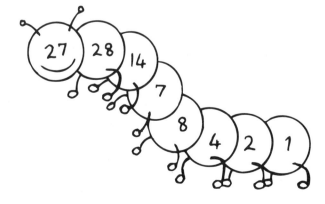

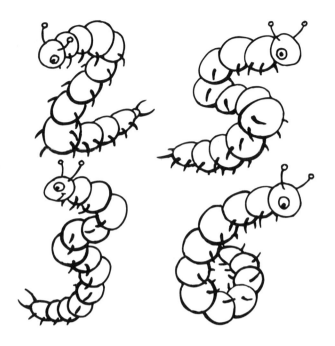

Recap the two operations you used to work out the numbers (halving and adding 1) and ask pupils how you decided which one to use. Hopefully, the children will be aware that you halved the even numbers and added one to the odd numbers. Explain this if necessary and ensure that everyone understands how you applied the rules.

Point to the centipede on the board and say: *This centipede has eight numbers. I want you to find the starting number which produces the longest possible centipede.* Explain that the starting number must be no bigger than 100 and pupils must stop when they get to 1. Hand out paper and pencils and set the children to work.

Plenary

Use a show of hands to find out how well pupils have done. Say to them: *Hands up if you found a centipede with exactly 10 numbers, 11 numbers, 12 numbers....* At various points ask a pupil who has raised his or her hand to tell you the starting number and quickly ask others in the class to work out subsequent numbers in the centipede. You could record the numbers on the board. Repeat this until you have discovered the starting number which produces the longest centipede (65 produces a centipede with 14 numbers).

Suggestion(s) for extension

Children who solve the initial problem could practise halving bigger numbers by choosing starting numbers up to 200.

Suggestion(s) for support

You may like to restrict the range of starting numbers for some pupils. These children could use starting numbers no bigger than 20 or 30.

Assessment opportunities

The children's written work will provide evidence of their ability to halve one and two-digit numbers without a calculator. During the main activity point to a particular number on a pupil's sheet and ask him or her to explain how it was halved. This will enable you to find out the mental strategies which are being used so that you can perhaps suggest more efficient alternatives.

Display ideas

The visual nature of the work produced by pupils makes it ideal for displaying. Pupils could shade in the body segments of their centipedes using two colours; one for odd numbers and one for even numbers.

DOUBLE OR HALVE BINGO

To practise mental doubling and halving strategies involving numbers up to 12.

†† *Whole-class activity.*

🕑 *Introduction 5–10 minutes; main activity 20–25 minutes; plenary 15–20 minutes; total 40–55 minutes.*

Previous skills/knowledge needed

Pupils should have some experience of doubling and halving whole numbers.

Key background information

During Key Stage One, the majority of pupils will have been introduced to doubling and halving, but these, like all mental strategies, need to be reinforced and practised regularly in a variety of contexts such as the game described here.

Preparation

For the main activity each pupil will need a 6 × 4 grid containing the numbers 1–24. Children could quickly draw such a grid themselves on squared paper at the start of the activity or, alternatively, you could produce a grid and make copies for the whole class. A twelve-sided dice, numbered 1–12, is also required although you could use two six-sided dice instead. You may also like to prepare a prompt sheet for less able children.

Resources

Number grids as described in 'Preparation', one twelve-sided dice (or two six-sided dice), squared paper, pencils, board/flip chart. For the support activity – a prompt sheet.

What to do

Introduction

Start with some quick-fire mental practice involving doubling and halving. The easiest way to do this is by simply calling out a number and asking the children to double it or halve it. You could concentrate on doubling first and then move on to halving or, alternatively, call out a number and ask one pupil to double it and another to halve it. Occasionally, stop and ask pupils to explain how they did the mental calculation and discuss the methods used and alternatives.

Main activity

Tell pupils to quickly produce a 6 × 4 grid containing the numbers 1–24. You might need to demonstrate this to them on the board or hold up an enlarged example for them to see. Alternatively give them a copy of the grid you have produced.

Explain how to play double or halve bingo. Tell pupils that you will roll a twelve-sided dice (or two six-sided dice) and they can either cross off the double of the dice score or half of the dice score. Stress that they can only do one

or the other, not both. The winner is the first person to cross off all of his or her numbers. Start to play the game by rolling the dice and allowing pupils a short period of time to cross a number off their grid. Keep a record of the dice scores so that any disputes can be resolved easily. After several rolls of the dice pause to check on progress by asking: *Who has crossed off five numbers altogether, …six numbers altogether* and so on. Hopefully, at some stage one of the pupils will point out that it is impossible to win, although you might need to provide a few hints or ask pointed questions such as: *Is anyone close to winning? Which numbers have you not crossed off? How long is it since you crossed off a number?*

Once it has been established that it is impossible to win the game, discuss the numbers that can and cannot be crossed off the grid and why. (7, 9, 11, 13, 15, 17, 19, 21 and 23 cannot be crossed off.) Then tell pupils that they are going to play the game again but this time they can decide which numbers appear on their grid. Tell them to draw another 6 × 4 grid and write in 24 numbers of their own choice. Stress that numbers can be written in more than once if they wish. Play the game again, reminding pupils of the rules, particularly that they can only cross off one number at a time.

When the game has been won, ask the winner and other pupils to explain which numbers they included on their grid and why. For example, some children may have chosen to include 2, 4 and 6 more often than other numbers because these can each be crossed off as a result of two dice scores. Discuss pupils' choices and reasons with the whole class.

If you have used two six-sided dice instead of a twelve-sided dice then this could add a new dimension to the discussion because some dice scores are more likely to occur than others. For example, a score of seven is more likely than a score of two because seven can be made in six different ways (1 + 6, 2 + 5, 3 + 4, 4 + 3, 5 + 2 and 6 +

1), whereas two can be made in only one way (1 + 1). However, if a twelve-sided dice is used then all twelve dice scores are equally likely. These issues could be discussed with an able group of pupils at the upper end of Key Stage Two.

Plenary

Discuss variations on the game, for example suppose you had used a ten-sided dice. Ask the children which numbers they would include on their number grids. What is the smallest and the biggest and which numbers would they not include? What about a twenty-sided dice? Again, which numbers would pupils include on their grids and which ones would they avoid?

Suggestion(s) for extension

The open-ended nature of the main activity means that it is self-differentiating and therefore the more able pupils will be able to work at their own level when deciding which numbers to include on the grid. Some of the variations discussed in the plenary, and the issue of using two six-sided dice, could form the basis of follow-up investigations for groups of able pupils.

Suggestion(s) for support

The nature of this activity is such that it should be accessible to all pupils. Less able children who find it very difficult to work out doubles and halves could be provided with a prompt sheet, for example a list of numbers up to 12 with doubles written at the side, or a multiplication tables grid.

Assessment opportunities

This activity produces very little tangible assessment evidence but by listening carefully to the children's responses during the discussions and by observing individuals during the main activity you will learn much about their understanding of doubles and halves.

Display ideas

Write brief instructions for the game on a piece of paper and display it on the wall. You could also display various 'Bingo cards' (6 × 4 grids) under two headings, 'You could win with these Bingo cards' and 'You cannot win with these Bingo cards – can you work out why?'

REMAINDERS

To divide two-digit numbers by single-digit numbers involving remainders.

†† *Whole-class introduction followed by a game in pairs and a whole-class plenary.*

⏱ *Introduction 10–15 minutes; main activity 25–30 minutes; plenary 10–15 minutes; total 45–60 minutes.*

Previous skills/knowledge needed

Children will need to be familiar with the concept of division by single-digit numbers, either with or without remainders. This activity can be used to introduce pupils to the idea of remainders if they have not already encountered them.

Key background information

Children usually encounter division for the first time in the context of halving; this is developed further to look at division by other single-digit numbers using language such as 'sharing', 'grouping' or 'lots of'. The calculations involved can be explained in terms of repeated addition ('counting on') repeated subtraction, or through knowledge of multiplication facts. Pupils need to spend much time developing an understanding of the concept of division and practising the associated skills, initially through problems which do not involve remainders. The next stage, presented in this activity, is to look at division with remainders.

Preparation

Make copies of photocopiable page 103 so that there is one for each pair. You may like to photocopy it onto coloured card or laminate it to make it more durable, particularly since the same card can be used for other activities in this book (see 'Round and round' on page 25).

Each pair will also need a six-sided dice but with the 1 changed to a 7 (or simply tell pupils to read the 1 as a 7). You may like to use photocopiable page 122 for those children carrying out the support activity in which case you will need to make sufficient copies.

Resources
Photocopiable page 103, six-sided dice, counters, paper, pencils. For the support activity – photocopiable page 122 (optional).

What to do
Introduction
Start a few minutes of quick-fire mental practice involving division without remainders. Then ask a question such as *What is 17 divided by 5?* and ask the children what they think the answer is. Discuss the division in the way you normally do (perhaps by counting on in 5s, by repeated subtraction of 5, or perhaps by using pupils' knowledge of multiplication facts) and draw out the fact that there is a remainder. Spend several more minutes asking further questions involving remainders and discussing the answers. Remember to ask pupils to explain the method they have used.

Main activity
Organize the children into pairs and give each pair a sheet of paper, a copy of photocopiable page 103 and a six-sided dice with the 1 replaced by a 7. One of the spaces on the track must be identified by you or the pupils as the starting point by marking it with a cross or colouring it in. Both pupils place their counter on the starting space and then take turns to roll the dice and move their counter in a clockwise direction according to the dice score. They must divide the number they land on by the score on the dice and write down the division, together with the answer, including any remainder, on their sheet of paper. The game ends once the first person has completed an agreed number of laps.

You could devise your own scoring system to find the winner. For example, the first person to complete the required number of laps scores five points plus one additional point for every problem answered correctly and the other player also scores one point for every correct answer.

While the children are playing the game, move around the groups and quickly mark their answers.

Plenary
Use this time for further quick-fire practice of division involving remainders. Another possibility is to pose questions such as: *Tell me a division which has a remainder of 3.* Open-ended questions such as this have many possible answers and so you could ask several pupils to provide an answer each time.

Suggestion(s) for extension
Some pupils could use ten or twelve-sided dice and therefore practise dividing by higher numbers.

Suggestion(s) for support
Less able children can practise dividing by a restricted range of numbers, for example, by 2, 5 and 10. Adapt a six-sided dice so that two sides show the number 2, two sides show 5 and two sides show 10. If you feel that some of the numbers on photocopiable page 103 are too big for these pupils then you could produce a number track of your own using photocopiable page 122.

Assessment opportunities
Pupils are required to record their calculations during the main activity so that you can assess their ability to divide with remainders. Also, make a mental note of pupils' responses during the quick-fire practice in the introduction and plenary.

Reference to photocopiable sheets
Photocopiable page 103 shows a racetrack with random numbers placed around it. A blank number track is provided on photocopiable page 122 so that you can produce tracks matched to the ability of the pupils in your class.

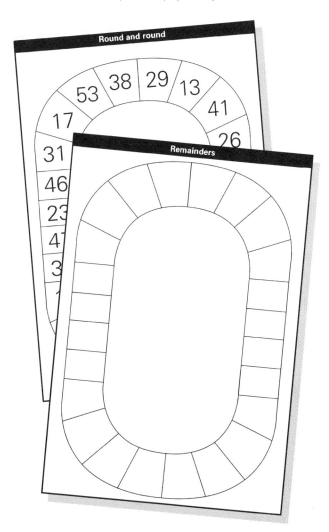

FROM 1 TO 100

To practise mental skills involving all four operations. To use brackets correctly in arithmetical expressions.

†† *Whole-class introduction followed by individual work and a whole-class plenary.*

🕐 *Introduction 10–15 minutes; main activity 25–30 minutes; plenary 10–15 minutes; total 45–60 minutes.*

Previous skills/knowledge needed

Children should be familiar with addition, subtraction, multiplication and division involving whole numbers.

Key background information

During Key Stages One and Two pupils spend a large proportion of their time learning and practising basic arithmetical skills. It is therefore important to make this work as varied and as interesting as possible rather than always presenting them with pages of 'sums'. The activity described below is open-ended in that children must find their own ways of making a particular answer and there is usually more than one way of doing it. The activity also introduces pupils to the use of brackets to denote precedence, that is, any calculations in brackets must be done first.

Preparation

Make copies of photocopiable pages 123 and 124 so that every pupil will have a copy of both sheets. Also try to get hold of two or three different types of calculator and check what answers you get when you type:

Some calculators will give the answer 35 while others give the answer 23. It would be really useful if you could find two calculators which give different answers.

Resources

Photocopiable pages 123 and 124, scrap paper, pencils, board/flip chart.

What to do

Introduction

Write 3 + 4 × 5 on the board and ask the children what they think the answer is. Most will probably do the arithmetic as they read it from left to right and so give the answer as 35. If this is the only answer that pupils give then say to them: *Does anyone think the answer could be something other than 35?* If a pupil suggests 23 then ask that child to explain how he or she got that answer. If nobody suggests 23 then give the two calculators to two pupils and ask them to key in the problem and call out the answer. Ask pupils to explain how the answer 23 has been produced. Ensure that all pupils appreciate that doing the calculations in a different order produces different answers.

Then say to the children: *Suppose I want you to work out 4 × 5 first. How could I show that on the board?* Some pupils might suggest drawing a box or a ring around that part, while some might already be aware of the use of brackets. Discuss the children's suggestions and eventually move on to explain that brackets are used to indicate which part of a calculation must be done first.

Write a few more examples on the board, ask pupils to work out the answers, and then discuss them briefly. Here are a few possibilities although you can easily make up your own.

$$12 + (8 \times 2)$$
$$21 \div (10 - 3)$$
$$(3 + 7) \times (8 - 5)$$

Main activity

Choose four digits, possibly by identifying a particular year, for example the year that most pupils in the class were born, or a year which corresponds to your history topic, or the year your school was built. Explain to the children that they must use these four digits to write pieces of arithmetic involving any operations that give the answers one, two, three, four, and so on up to 100. They do not have to use all four digits each time but they can only use each digit once (unless that digit appears twice in the year for example if you have used 1994 the children can use two 9s). Get pupils started by working through the first few answers on the board. Say to them *How can I use these digits to make the answer 1?* Record the arithmetic

Assessment opportunities

The children's written work will provide evidence of their arithmetical skills and in some cases their ability to use brackets correctly. Watch out for errors and misconceptions during the main activity and discuss these with individual pupils.

Display ideas

This activity could form the basis of an on-going interactive display. Make a poster-size version of photocopiable pages 123 and 124 and use it to display one way of making each of the numbers from 1 to 100. It is likely that there will be many gaps in the display but these can be filled in as and when pupils find additional solutions over a period of two or three weeks.

Reference to photocopiable sheets

Photocopiable pages 123 and 124 show the numbers 1–50 and 51–100 respectively. In the spaces beside each number the children have to fill in a calculation showing how they made that particular number using up to four digits and any of the four arithmetical operations.

on the board and then ask them to make the answer 2, the answer 3 and the answer 4. Here are a few examples using the year 1994.

$$9 + 1 - 9 = 1$$
$$1 + (9 \div 9) = 2$$
$$94 - 91 = 3$$
$$1 \times 4 = 4$$

Remind pupils that they can use any operations, they can use brackets and they can combine the digits to make two- or three-digit numbers (as in 91 and 94 above). Give out copies of photocopiable pages 123 and 124 for the children to record their work on and make scrap paper available for rough calculations. Tell pupils that they do not necessarily have to work through from 1 to 100 in order (unless you specifically want them to do so).

Plenary

Use a show of hands to quickly find out which numbers between 1 and 100 have and have not been made, by asking: *Who has made 1? Who has made 2?* and so on. If only a single pupil has managed to make a particular number then ask that child to explain how he or she did it, or to come out and write it on the board. Also give some of the less able pupils an opportunity to provide solutions.

Suggestion(s) for extension

The open-ended nature of this activity is such that it should present a challenge for even the most able pupils.

Suggestion(s) for support

Since differentiation is by outcome all the children should be able to get started on the activity and make progress. Pupils will work at their own level, using operations with which they are familiar.

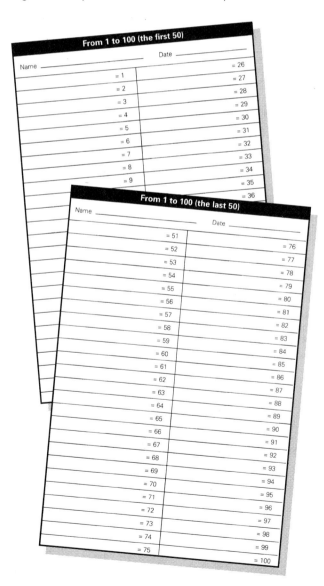

THREE IN A ROW

To practise mental skills involving a variety of arithmetical operations in the context of a strategy game.

†† *Whole-class introduction followed by a game in pairs and a whole-class plenary.*

🕐 *Introduction 10–15 minutes; main activity 25–30 minutes; plenary 10–15 minutes; total 45–60 minutes.*

Previous skills/knowledge needed

This activity is self-differentiating in that children will only need to use the arithmetical operations they choose to and so the minimum requirement is to be able to add two single-digit numbers mentally.

Key background information

Sound mental arithmetic skills provide the basis for successful number work and so it is vital that these skills are practised regularly. However, it is important to do this in a wide variety of contexts so as to avoid unnecessary repetition and boredom. The game described here provides one possible context.

Preparation

You will need sufficient copies of photocopiable page 125 to allow one between two pupils. Each pair will also need a pack of twenty or thirty cards containing numbers in the range 1–10. You can use photocopiable page 94 to produce these if necessary. Make one copy of the sheet, change the zero to a ten, and then photocopy the sheet onto coloured card. Use a different colour for each pack so that

pupils sitting close to one another do not get the cards mixed up. An alternative to using a pack of cards is to use a ten-sided dice. These are usually numbered 0 to 9 and so again you will need to change the zero to a ten. If you are going to carry out the 'Suggestion(s) for extension and support' opposite you will need to alter photocopiable page 125 accordingly.

Resources

Photocopiable page 125, packs of 1–10 cards as described in 'Preparation' (or ten-sided dice), a supply of counters in two colours, calculators, paper, pencils.

What to do

Introduction

Start the lesson with a few minutes of quick-fire mental arithmetic practice involving a variety of operations. You could call out questions for pupils to answer and also reverse the process, so that you call out an answer and pupils must provide the question.

Next, pick two cards from a set of 1–10 number cards and write the two numbers on the board. Ask the children what answers can be made using these two numbers and the different arithmetical operations. Record the arithmetic on the board. For example, the numbers 3 and 9 can be used to produce the answers 12, 6, 27 and 3. Repeat this using two new cards.

Main activity

Tell the children to work with a partner and give each pair one copy of photocopiable page 125, a set of 1–10 number cards, counters in two colours and one calculator. Player one picks two cards from the set of number cards (or rolls a ten-sided dice twice) and decides how she wants to combine them to produce an answer. She must tell the other player how the numbers have been combined and what the answer is. If the answer is correct (player two can check with a calculator if necessary) she can cover a square that contains the answer with one of her counters. Players must also record their arithmetic on paper so that you can check it later. Then it is player two's turn.

The objective is for each player to get three counters of their own colour in a row horizontally, vertically or diagonally, just like noughts and crosses. After picking two number cards, pupils will hopefully calculate the possible answers and then choose the one which is most beneficial to them. This quick consideration of the possibilities should develop mental arithmetic skills.

Plenary
Focus discussion on the strategies used during the game. Ask pupils to explain how they decided which of the possible answers to go for.

Provide additional mental practice by asking pupils to tell you the biggest possible answer that can be made when you pick two cards from a set of 1–10 number cards ($10 \times 10 = 100$) and also the smallest answer ($1 \times 1 = 1$). Then ask them to think of a number less than 100 which cannot be made. Compile a list on the board. This should result in much valuable discussion.

Suggestion(s) for extension
This activity can be extended in various ways. For example, children could use a set of cards numbered 1–15 or 1–20 (or roll a twelve or twenty-sided dice twice). Photocopiable page 125 would need to be modified, for example if 1–15 number cards are used the numbers on the corresponding grid would need to go up to 225. Not all numbers in the range 1–225 can be made, so it would be important to choose those numbers to be included on the grid very carefully.

Another possibility is to ask pupils to pick three cards from a set of 1–10 number cards and use combinations of arithmetical operations. Again, a modified grid would need to be used.

The variations are endless. Different numbers of cards can be selected from different types of sets according to the ability of the pupils.

Suggestion(s) for support
Less able pupils who need to focus just on addition and subtraction could use a modified grid containing only numbers up to 20.

Assessment opportunities
Observing the children while they play the game will provide valuable information about their ability to calculate mentally. Also, by requiring pupils to record their calculations on paper during the game you will be able to monitor their progress.

Reference to photocopiable sheet
Photocopiable page 125 provides a number grid. Using the four arithmetical operations and a pack of 1–10 number cards, the children have to make answers and cover the corresponding number on the grid with their counters.

Three in a row						
12	60	1	48	16	4	24
28	36	17	21	7	11	0
6	2	10	72	5	30	19
40	13	20	3	45	15	63
8	54	0	2	9	35	6
1	32	4	18	42	27	2
90	3	80	1	14	5	56

THREE DICE BINGO

To practise mental calculation skills involving a variety of operations.

†† *Whole-class introduction followed by a game in small groups and a whole-class plenary.*

🕐 *Introduction 10–15 minutes; main activity 25–30 minutes; plenary 10–15 minutes; total 45–60 minutes.*

Previous skills/knowledge needed
Pupils will need to be familiar with the four rules of number and be able to apply these using single-digit numbers.

Key background information
This activity provides another opportunity for children to practise their mental skills using a variety of operations involving two or more numbers. It can be used as an alternative to doing pages of 'sums' and the nature of the activity is such that it should challenge and motivate pupils.

Preparation
Make copies of photocopiable page 126 so that there is one per pupil. Also ensure that there are sufficient six-sided dice for each group to have three during the main activity. Use photocopiable page 94 to produce a set of 0–

9 number cards which are required during the introduction. If you are carrying out the 'Suggestion(s) for extension and support', you will need to modify photocopiable page 126 accordingly.

Resources

Photocopiable page 126, one set of 0–9 number cards, six-sided dice, pencils.

What to do

Introduction

Start with some quick-fire mental calculation practice using numbers up to 10 and a variety of operations. Then ask three pupils to each pick a card from your set of 0–9 number cards and write the numbers on the board. Invite the children to make answers from the numbers using any operations they want to. They can use any two of the numbers or all three. Record the arithmetic on the board. You might like to use this as an opportunity to revise or introduce brackets to denote precedence, that is, any arithmetic in brackets is worked out first (see the activity 'From 1 to 100' on page 82 for further details of how to introduce brackets).

Main activity

Organize the children into small groups, distribute the copies of photocopiable page 126 and explain how to play three dice bingo. Each player takes it in turns to roll the three dice. The pupil who rolls the dice then has a set amount of time (say, 30 seconds) to make up to five different answers in the range 1–30. Each answer that is made can be crossed off the bingo card at the top of photocopiable page 126 while the arithmetic used to make the numbers is recorded in the boxes underneath. Play then passes to the next pupil. The aim is for pupils to cross off all of the numbers on their bingo card.

Plenary

Use the plenary for further quick-fire mental practice by running through possible ways of making each of the numbers from 1 to 30 using two or three dice scores. You can make this more challenging by insisting that all three dice scores must be used each time ($6 \times 5 = 30$ for example is not permitted).

Suggestion(s) for extension

This activity can be developed in various ways, for example ten or twelve-sided dice could be used. The range of numbers on the bingo card will then need to be extended appropriately.

Suggestion(s) for support

The nature of the main activity is such that it should be accessible to all pupils since they will work at their own level and so differentiation is by outcome. However, you might want to reduce the range of numbers on some pupils' bingo cards to, for example, 1–20.

Assessment opportunities

The purpose of making pupils record their arithmetic is so that you can check it, either during the main activity or afterwards. Observe the children carefully during the main activity to see how quickly they are able to calculate mentally.

Reference to photocopiable sheet

Photocopiable page 126 shows the numbers 1–30. Using three dice and the four arithmetical operations, the children have to attempt to cross off all the numbers. Space is provided on the photocopiable sheet for them to show how they arrived at their answers.

Three dice Bingo					
Name				Date	
1	2	3	4	5	6
7	8	9	10	11	12
13	14	15	16	17	18
19	20	21	22	23	24
25	26	27	28	29	30

FIND...

To practise mental calculation skills involving a variety of operations.

†† *Whole-class introduction followed by individual work and whole-class plenary.*

🕐 *Introduction 10–15 minutes; main activity 25–30 minutes; plenary 10–15 minutes; total 45–60 minutes.*

Previous skills/knowledge needed

It is assumed that pupils are already familiar with the four rules of number and have some experience of applying them using one and two-digit numbers.

Key background information

This open-ended activity provides pupils with a valuable opportunity to consolidate and practise important number skills which have been introduced on earlier occasions. Pupils need this sort of practice throughout Key Stage Two but it is important to use a variety of contexts rather than relying only on pages of 'sums'. The activity described below requires pupils to use a number grid to find pairs or groups of numbers which satisfy particular conditions based on addition, subtraction, multiplication and division. It is possible to adapt the activity to suit pupils of all abilities.

Preparation

Make copies of photocopiable pages 125 and 127 so that there is one of each sheet per pupil. If you are carrying out the 'Suggestion(s) for extension and support' then you may need to modify these sheets accordingly. Also make a copy of this number grid on the board. You will need to refer to it during the introduction.

4	9	6	13
15	3	8	9
2	10	5	11
7	8	12	1

Resources

Photocopiable pages 125 and 127, paper, pencils.

What to do

Introduction

Start with a few minutes of quick-fire mental calculation practice involving a variety of operations. Ask open-ended questions such as: *Tell me three numbers with a sum of 20. Tell me two numbers with a difference of 12. Tell me two numbers with a product of 18,* and so on. You might need to recap or introduce terminology such as 'sum', 'difference' and 'product'.

Draw the children's attention to the number grid you have written on the board and use this as the basis for further mental practice. If you have made an exact copy of the grid shown in 'Preparation' then all of the following problems can be posed.

▲ *Find two numbers that are next to one another and add up to 15.*

▲ *Find two numbers that are next to one another and add up to 20.*

▲ *Find three numbers in a vertical line that add up to 25.*

▲ *Find three numbers in a horizontal line that add up to 20.*

▲ *Find three numbers in a diagonal line that add up to 25.*

▲ *Find pairs of numbers next to one another with a difference of 5.*

▲ *Find two numbers next to one another with a product of 45.*

▲ *Find three numbers in a line with a product of 100.*

Use these examples and other similar problems of your own, remembering to match the problems to the ability of the pupil who responds. You might need to explain some of the language associated with these questions, for example 'horizontal', 'diagonal', 'vertical', 'row' and 'column'.

Main activity

Give out one copy of photocopiable pages 125 and 127 and some paper to each pupil. Explain that the children must look at the number grid on photocopiable page 125 and find the pairs or sets of numbers specified on page 127. When they have found the numbers they must record them on paper. This could be in the form of arithmetic using numbers and symbols, for example 8 x 5 = 40, or it could be in the form of a drawing indicating the numbers and their orientation on the grid, for example:

8
5

If any children complete the photocopiable sheet then ask them to work through it again and to find a second solution to each question. There are at least two solutions to each question apart from the targets in question 5 which have only one.

Plenary

Work through some or all of the answers. Bear in mind that in almost every case the total can be made in more than one way. Also ask pupils to explain how they went about finding the totals.

Suggestion(s) for extension

Photocopiable page 127 provides examples of the sorts of targets you could set. It should be very easy for you to make up other more challenging sheets based on the same number grid or on other grids which you have easy access to. Alternatively, you could make a grid of your own which includes bigger numbers. Another extension activity is to ask pupils to set targets of their own based on the original grid and pass these on to other pupils to find.

Suggestion(s) for support

It should be possible for less able pupils to answer the early questions on the sheet, for example finding two numbers which add up to 20 or two numbers with a difference of 2. If you feel that this is their limit then ask

them to answer these questions in as many ways as possible (there are at least three solutions to each part of question 1 and four solutions to each part of question 2).

If you feel that many of the questions are too demanding for some pupils then make a list of easier targets based on the original grid or perhaps based on a new grid of your own containing lower numbers.

Assessment opportunities

The work recorded on paper will indicate pupils' ability to calculate mentally. Also observe how they tackle the main activity and ask them to explain what they are doing. This will provide an insight into the way they work with number as well as their ability to use and apply mathematics.

Display ideas

An enlarged copy of the original grid could be displayed on the wall together with pupils' solutions to the questions. This could form the basis of an on-going attempt to find all the different ways of answering each question. Children could add new solutions to the display as they find them.

Reference to photocopiable sheets

Photocopiable page 127 poses a number of problems which the children have to work out using photocopiable page 125. The solutions are as follows:

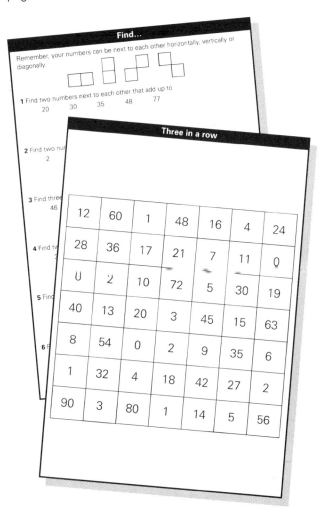

Question 1

Two numbers that add up to 20

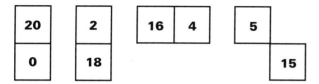

Two numbers with a difference of 15

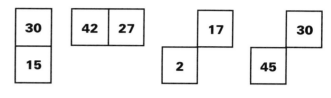

Two numbers that add up to 30

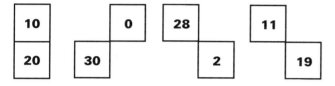

Two numbers with a difference of 20

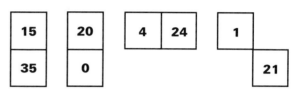

Two numbers that add up to 35

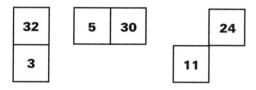

Two numbers with a difference of 32

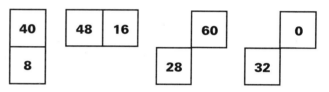

Two numbers that add up to 48

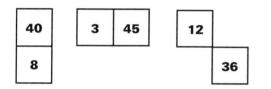

Question 3

Three numbers that add up to 46

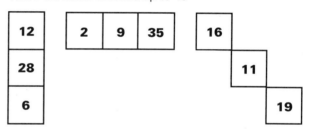

Two numbers that add up to 77

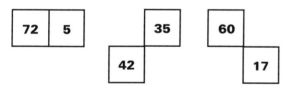

Three numbers that add up to 59

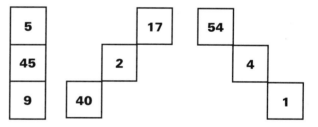

Question 2

Two numbers with a difference of 2

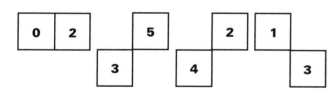

Three numbers that add up to 64

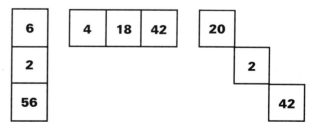

Two numbers with a difference of 9

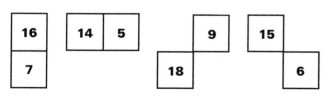

Three numbers that add up to 77

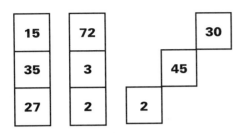

Three numbers that add up to 99

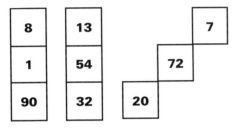

Question 4

Two numbers with a product of 36

Two numbers with a product of 54

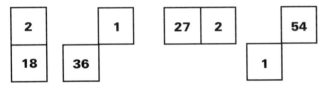

Two numbers with a product of 70

Two numbers with a product of 90

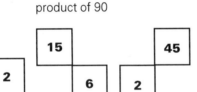

Two numbers with a product of 96

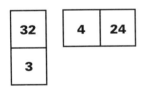

Question 5

Three numbers with a product of 24

Three numbers with a product of 80

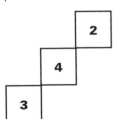
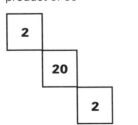

Three numbers with a product of 108

Three numbers with a product of 120

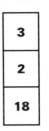
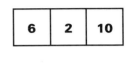

Three numbers with a product of 270

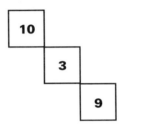

Question 6

Two numbers with a product of 135

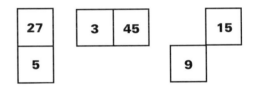

Two numbers with a product of 210

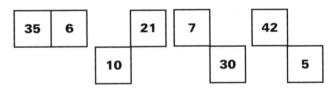

Two numbers with a product of 216

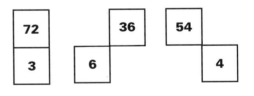

Two numbers with a product of 240

Two numbers with a product of 360

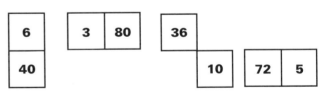

TIMES AND DATES

To practise mental skills involving a variety of arithmetical operations. To use and apply knowledge of time and date notation.

†† *Whole-class introduction followed by individual work and a whole-class plenary.*

⏲ *Introduction 15–20 minutes; main activity 20–25 minutes; plenary 10–15 minutes; total 45–60 minutes.*

Previous skills/knowledge needed
Children will need to be able to use the four rules of number with one and two-digit whole numbers. They will also need to be familiar with 24-hour clock notation.

Key background information
This activity provides children with an unusual context for practising their arithmetic skills and also allows them to revise and consolidate their knowledge of the conventions used to denote times and dates.

Preparation
Make copies of photocopiable page 128 so that there is one for each child and write this description of a particular moment in time on the board.

Twenty-six minutes to one on June 5th 1978

Resources
Photocopiable page 128, paper, pencils, board/flip chart.

What to do
Introduction
Point to the time and date written on the board and say to pupils: *Can you spot what was special about this particular moment in time?* It is unlikely that anyone will spot the significance so you will have to provide further clues. Say to pupils: *Tell me another way of writing twenty-six minutes to one.* Record the answer on the board (12.34). Then say: *How could we write June 5th 1978?* and record it on the board to the right of the time so that you have this on the board.

12.34 5/6/78

Pupils should now be able to spot that the eight digits in the time and date are consecutive, although you might have to introduce and explain this particular word.

Spend the next few minutes focusing on time related questions, for example: *Tell me another time during the day when the digits on a digital clock are consecutive.* The possibilities are 1.23, 2.34, 3.45, 4.56 and 23.45. Use the final solution as a way of revising 24-hour clock

notation. Then use this notation as the basis of some quick-fire mental practice by posing problems such as: *Tell me a time when the hours and the minutes add up to 20* (for instance 5.15 or quarter-past-five). *Tell me a time when the difference between the hours and minutes is 15* (20.05 or five-past-eight in the evening). *Tell me a time when the product of the hours and minutes is 40* (2.20 or twenty-past-two). There are several different times which satisfy each of these questions so invite answers from more than one pupil and also ask them to give the time in both ways so as to reinforce their understanding of ways of telling the time.

The quick-fire mental calculation practice can be extended to include dates by asking questions such as: *Tell me a date this year when the sum of the day and month is 15* (7th August). *Tell me a date when the difference between the day and month is 10* (22nd December). *Tell me a date when the product of the day and month is 40* (8th May). Again, there is more than one solution to each question so invite answers from more than one pupil.

Main activity
Give out copies of photocopiable page 128 and ask pupils to complete the questions, recording their answers on paper.

Plenary
Spend some time going through some or all of the answers to the questions on the photocopiable sheet. Ensure that the less able pupils are given an opportunity to provide some of the solutions.

Then remind pupils of the special moment in time which you wrote on the board earlier (it might still be there for pupils to see). Say to them: *Can anyone think of another moment in time when this has happened?* The possibilities are

0.12 on 3/4/56
1.23 on 4/5/67
2.34 on 5/6/78
3.45 on 6/7/89
23.45 on 6/7/89

Suggestion(s) for extension
All of the questions on the photocopiable sheet have a large number of possible answers and so those pupils who complete the sheet could go back and find additional solutions. You might want some pupils to investigate the final question posed in the plenary section above.

Suggestion(s) for support
Most of the questions should be accessible to all pupils in the class although you might want to restrict some pupils to particular questions, for example just those involving addition and subtraction.

Assessment opportunities

Pupils written work will provide written evidence of their mental skills and also their understanding of the notation used to denote times and dates. Observe pupils carefully during the main activity, check their solutions and discuss any errors or misconceptions.

Display ideas

Some of the themes explored in this activity could form the basis of an on-going display under the heading 'What is special about these times and dates – Can you find any more like these?'

Reference to photocopiable sheet

Photocopiable page 128 poses a number of problems relating to times and dates which the children have to solve.

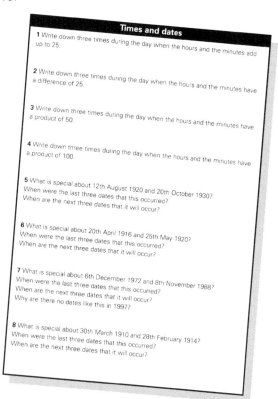

Times and dates

1 Write down three times during the day when the hours and the minutes add up to 25.

2 Write down three times during the day when the hours and the minutes have a difference of 25.

3 Write down three times during the day when the hours and the minutes have a product of 50.

4 Write down three times during the day when the hours and the minutes have a product of 100.

5 What is special about 12th August 1920 and 20th October 1930? When were the last three dates that this occurred? When are the next three dates that it will occur?

6 What is special about 20th April 1916 and 25th May 1920? When were the last three dates that this occurred? When are the next three dates that it will occur?

7 What is special about 6th December 1972 and 8th November 1988? When were the last three dates that this occurred? When are the next three dates that it will occur? Why are there no dates like this in 1997?

8 What is special about 30th March 1910 and 28th February 1914? When were the last three dates that this occurred? When are the next three dates that it will occur?

Question 1: There are many possible answers e.g. 5.20 and 20.05.

Question 2: There are many possible answers, for example 0.25 and 10.35.

Question 3: Only four possible answers – 1.50, 2.25, 5.10 and 10.05.

Question 4: Only five possible answers – 2.50, 4.25, 5.20, 10.10 and 20.05.

Question 5: The day and the month add to give the year. The last three occasions are 29/12/41,

30/12/42 and 31/12/43. The next three occasions are 1/1/02, 2/1/03 and 1/2/03.

Question 6: Subtract the month from the day to give the year. The last three occasions are 31/3/28, 30/1/29 and 31/1/30. There are twelve occasions during the year 2000 i.e. 1/1/00, 2/2/00 etc. The next three occasions after that are 2/1/01, 3/2/01 and 4/3/01.

Question 7: The year is the product of the day and the month. The answers obviously depend on when the activity is actually being carried out. Recent and forthcoming occasions are 24/4/96, 16/6/96, 12/8/96, 8/12/96, 14/7/98, 11/9/99, 9/11/99, 1/1/01, 2/1/02 and 1/2/02. There are no dates like this in 1997 because 97 is a prime number.

Question 8: Divide the day by the month to give the year. The last three occasions are 29/1/29, 30/1/30 and 31/1/31. The next three occasions are 1/1/01, 2/2/01 and 3/3/01. You could make this question more challenging by telling pupils that they must not use a 1 for the day, month or year. The solutions to this are 28/2/14, 26/2/13, 24/2/12, 4/2/02, 6/3/02 and 8/4/02.

Place value dice games, see page 13

Dice games

Name _____   Date _____

Points Scored

Game 1	□ □	<	□ □							□
Game 2	□ □	<	□ □							□
Game 3	□ □	<	□ □							□
Game 4	□ □	<	□ □							□
Game 5	□ □	+	□ □							□
Game 6	□ □	+	□ □							□
Game 7	□ □	+	□ □							□
Game 8	□ □	+	□ □							□
Game 9	□ □	+	□ □							□
Game 10	□ □	+	□ □							□
Game 11	□ □	<	□ □	<	□ □					□
Game 12	□ □	<	□ □	<	□ □					□
Game 13	□ □	<	□ □	<	□ □					□
Game 14	□ □	<	□ □	<	□ □					□

Place value dice games, see page 13; Three in a row, see page 84; Three dice Bingo, see page 85

0–9 digit cards

0	1	2
3	4	5
6	7	8
	9	

0–9 digit cards

PHOTOCOPIABLES

Tens, hundreds and thousands, see page 16

Tens, hundreds and thousands

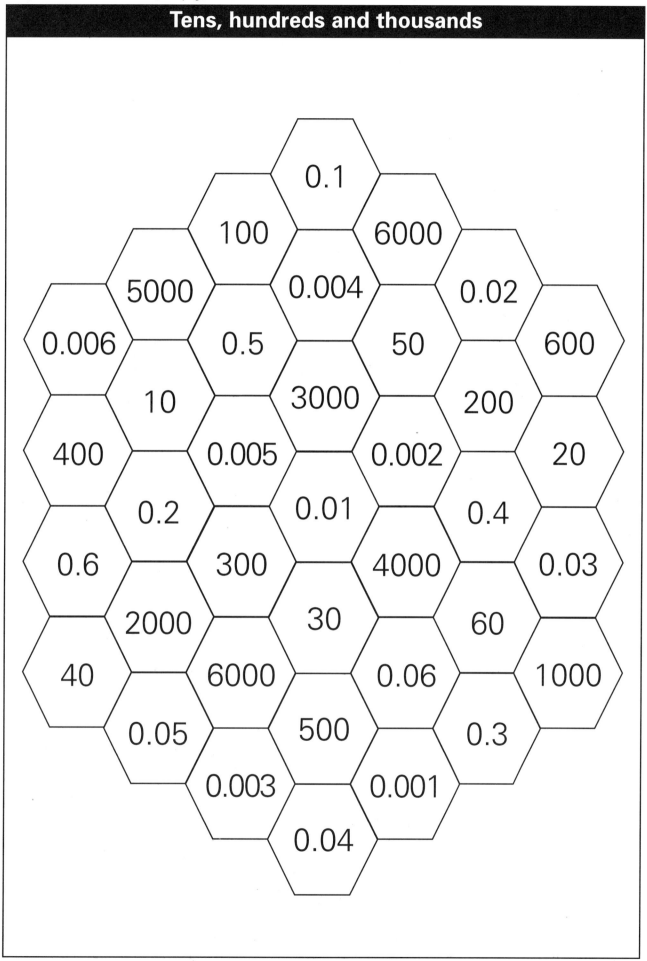

NUMBER KEY STAGE TWO

95

Fractions with pattern blocks, see page 18

Fractions with pattern blocks (1)

Fill the shapes on the worksheets with pattern blocks.

Small hexagon
Half of one colour, half of another.
One third of one colour, two thirds of another.

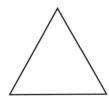

Triangle
Half of one colour, half of another.
One third of one colour, two thirds of another.

Star
Half of one colour, half of another.
One quarter of one colour, three quarters of another.
One third of one colour, two thirds of another.
One sixth of one colour, five sixths of another.

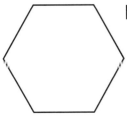

Large hexagon
Half of one colour, half of another.
One quarter of one colour, three quarters of another.
One third of one colour, two thirds of another.
One sixth of one colour, five sixths of another.
One eighth of one colour, seven eighths of another.
Three eighths of one colour, five eighths of another.

Fractions with pattern blocks, see page 18

Fractions with pattern blocks (2)

Name _____ Date _____

Fractions with pattern blocks, see page 18

Fractions with pattern blocks (3)

Name _____   Date _____

NUMBER KEY STAGE TWO

Fractions with pattern blocks, see page 18

Fractions with pattern blocks (4)

Name _____ Date _____

Congruent halves

1. Copy each of these shapes onto spotted paper and divide each one into congruent halves (one of them is impossible).

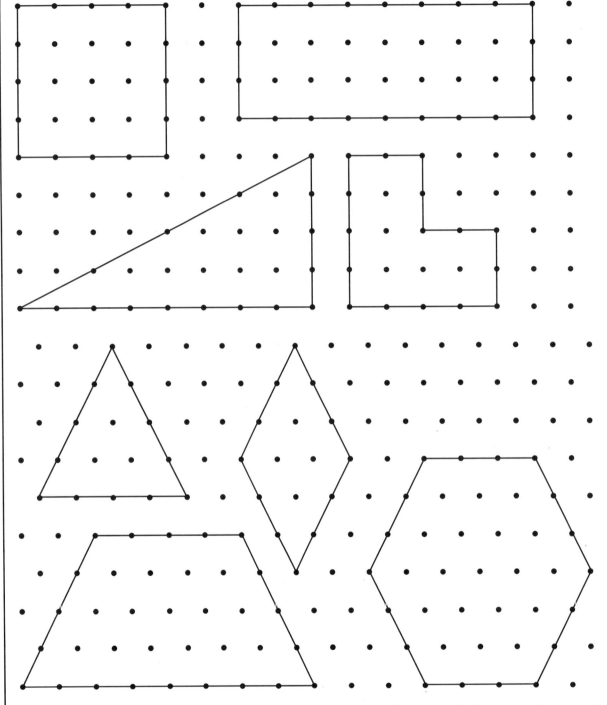

2. Copy the shapes onto spotted paper again and divide each one into congruent quarters.

3. Copy the shapes onto spotted paper again and divide each one into congruent thirds (one of them is impossible).

Congruent halves, see page 21

Square spotted paper

Name _____   Date _____

Congruent halves, see page 21

Triangular spotted paper

Name _____   Date _____

Round and round, see page 25; Remainders, see page 80

Round and round

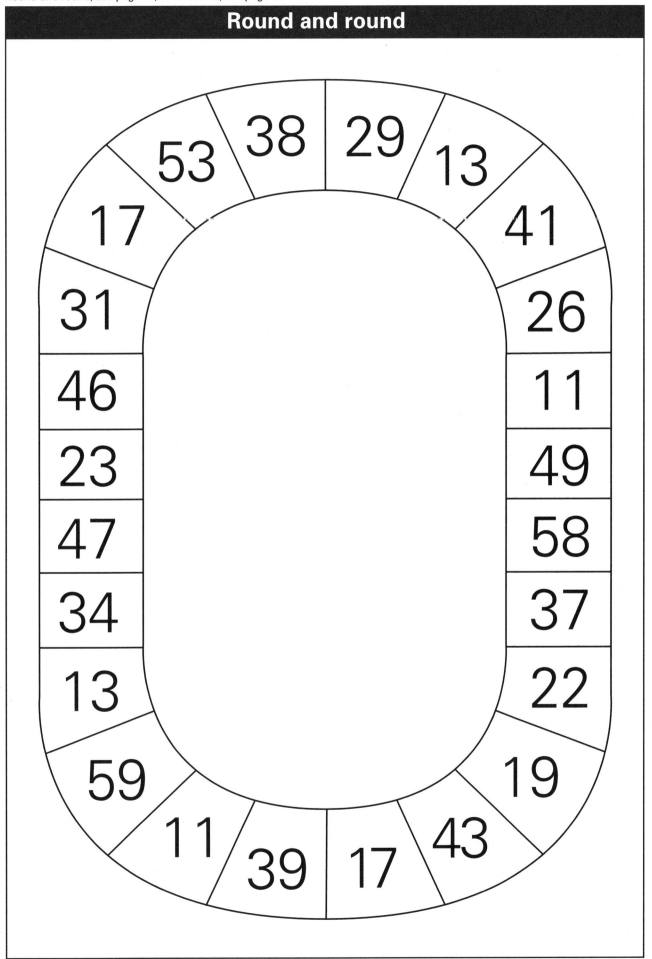

Multilink primes, see page 28; Neighbours, see page 40; Pentominoes on a 100-square, see page 62

Multilink primes

Name _____ Date _____

1	2	3	4	5	6	7	8	9	10
11	12	13	14	15	16	17	18	19	20
21	22	23	24	25	26	27	28	29	30
31	32	33	34	35	36	37	38	39	40
41	42	43	44	45	46	47	48	49	50
51	52	53	54	55	56	57	58	59	60
61	62	63	64	65	66	67	68	69	70
71	72	73	74	75	76	77	78	79	80
81	82	83	84	85	86	87	88	89	90
91	92	93	94	95	96	97	98	99	100

NUMBER KEY STAGE TWO

Set search, see page 30

Set search

Name _____   Date _____

▲ Find the sets and sequences of numbers listed below on the grid.
Put a ring around each one.
(Hint: There should be six numbers in each set or sequence.)
One of the sets or sequences cannot be found on the grid.
Can you work out which one?

Odd numbers
Even numbers
Multiples of 3
Multiples of 4
Multiples of 5
Multiples of 6
Multiples of 7
Multiples of 8
Multiples of 9
Multiples of 10
Square numbers
Triangular numbers
Prime numbers
Factors of 12
Factors of 18
Factors of 20
Factors of 28

2	11	9	7	5	3	1	4	1	7
5	8	13	4	2	6	5	8	2	3
17	1	2	3	6	9	18	12	4	1
1	2	3	4	6	12	7	16	5	4
2	4	5	6	11	15	18	20	10	9
4	7	7	2	10	18	5	24	20	16
6	14	11	5	10	15	20	25	30	25
8	28	13	6	1	2	21	1	40	36
10	7	14	21	28	35	42	9	50	12
12	4	9	18	27	36	45	63	60	3

Ups and downs, see page 31

Ups and downs

100	99	98	97	96	95	94	93	92	91
81	82	83	84	85	86	87	88	89	90
80	79	78	77	76	75	74	73	72	71
61	62	63	64	65	66	67	68	69	70
60	59	58	57	56	55	54	53	52	51
41	42	43	44	45	46	47	48	49	50
40	39	38	37	36	35	34	33	32	31
21	22	23	24	25	26	27	28	29	30
20	19	18	17	16	15	14	13	12	11
1	2	3	4	5	6	7	8	9	10

Fibonacci Towers, see page 33

Fibonacci Towers (1)

Name _____   Date _____

1 Complete the Fibonnaci sequence in Tower 1.
2 Shade the even numbers with a coloured pencil. What do you notice?

_____

_____

3 Shade the multiple of 3 using a different colour. What do you notice?

_____

_____

4 Shade the multiples of 5 in another colour. What do you notice?

_____

_____

5 Write two different numbers in the top two boxes of Tower 2. Fill in the other boxes using the same adding rule as the Fibonacci sequence.
6 Repeat questions 2, 3 and 4 using Tower 2.
Are the shadings on Tower 2 the same as on Tower 1?

_____

Tower 1	Tower 2
1	
1	
2	
3	
5	

Fibonacci Towers, see page 33

Fibonacci Towers (2)

Name _____   Date _____

7 Use the numbers in Tower 1. Divide the second number by the first number. Record your answer in the top box of the 'Tower 1 Division Answers' column.

Then divide the third number by the second number and record the answer in the next box of the 'Tower 1 Division Answers' column. Divide every number by the number above and record the answer in the 'Tower 1 Division Answers' column. Note: Use a calculator and give answers to 2 decimal places.

What do you notice about the answers?

_____

_____

8 Repeat question 7 using the numbers in Tower 2. Record your answers in the 'Tower 2 Division Answers' column.

What happens this time?

_____

Tower 1 Division Answers	Tower 2 Division Answers

NUMBER KEY STAGE TWO

Palindromes, see page 35

Palindromes

Name _____   Date _____

1 Find and write a palindrome which is

- a multiple of 3 _____
- a multiple of 4 _____
- a multiple of 5 _____
- a multiple of 6 _____
- a multiple of 7 _____
- a multiple of 8 _____
- a multiple of 9 _____
- a multiple of 11 _____
- a multiple of 12 _____

> Madam, I'm Adam

Why do you think there are no palindromes which are multiples of 10?

_____

2 Find and write down a palindrome which is

- a square number _____
- a triangular number _____
- a prime number _____

3 Find and write down two palindromes which have

- a difference of 2 _____
- a difference of 10 _____
- a difference which is a palindrome _____
- a product which is a palindrome _____

Maths with a calendar (1)

Name _____   Date _____

1 Work out the sum of the numbers in the first column.

_____

Which column has a sum of 80?

_____

January						
M	**T**	**W**	**T**	**F**	**S**	**S**
		1	2	3	4	5
6	7	8	9	10	11	12
13	14	15	16	17	18	19
20	21	22	23	24	25	26
27	28	29	30	31		

2 Work out the sum of the numbers in the top row.

_____

Which row has a sum of 145?

_____

3 Find three numbers which are next to one another in a horizontal line and have a sum of 75.

_____

4 Find three numbers which are next to one another in a vertical line and have a sum of 45.

_____

5 Find three numbers which are next to one another in a diagonal line and have a sum of 54.

_____

6 Look carefully at your answers to questions 3, 4 and 5. Compare the middle number with the sum of the three numbers. What do you notice?

_____

Maths with a calendar (2)

Name _____   Date _____

7 A square has been drawn on the calendar.
The sum of the four numbers in the square is 20.
Find four numbers which form a square and have a sum of 60.

_____

		January				
M	**T**	**W**	**T**	**F**	**S**	**S**
		1	2	3	4	5
6	7	8	9	10	11	12
13	14	15	16	17	18	19
20	21	22	23	24	25	26
27	28	29	30	31		

8 Choose any four numbers which form a square.

_____

Work out the difference between the biggest and smallest number.
Do this for another four numbers which form a square and then for another four numbers.
What do you notice?

_____

9 Use the four numbers with the square drawn around them.
Multiply the numbers diagonally (1 x 9).
Multiply the other two numbers diagonally (2 x 8).
Work out the difference between the two answers.

_____

Do this again for another four numbers which form a square and then for another four numbers.
What do you notice?

_____

_____

Football strips, see page 54

Football strips

Name _____ Date _____

FURTHER *Curriculum Bank* ACTIVITIES
PHOTOCOPIABLES

Input-output machines (1)

Name _____ Date _____

Input	Output

Input	Output

Input	Output

Input	Output

Input	Output

Input	Output

Input	Output

Input	Output

Input	Output

Input-output machines, see page 59

Input-output machines (2)

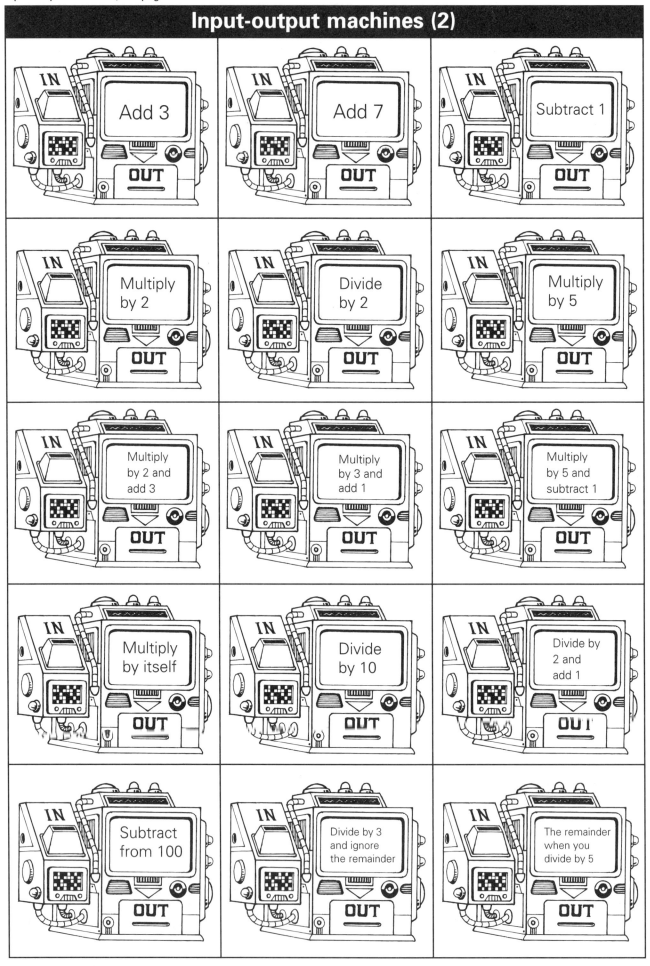

Add 3

Add 7

Subtract 1

Multiply by 2

Divide by 2

Multiply by 5

Multiply by 2 and add 3

Multiply by 3 and add 1

Multiply by 5 and subtract 1

Multiply by itself

Divide by 10

Divide by 2 and add 1

Subtract from 100

Divide by 3 and ignore the remainder

The remainder when you divide by 5

Input-output machines, see page 59

Input-output machines (3)

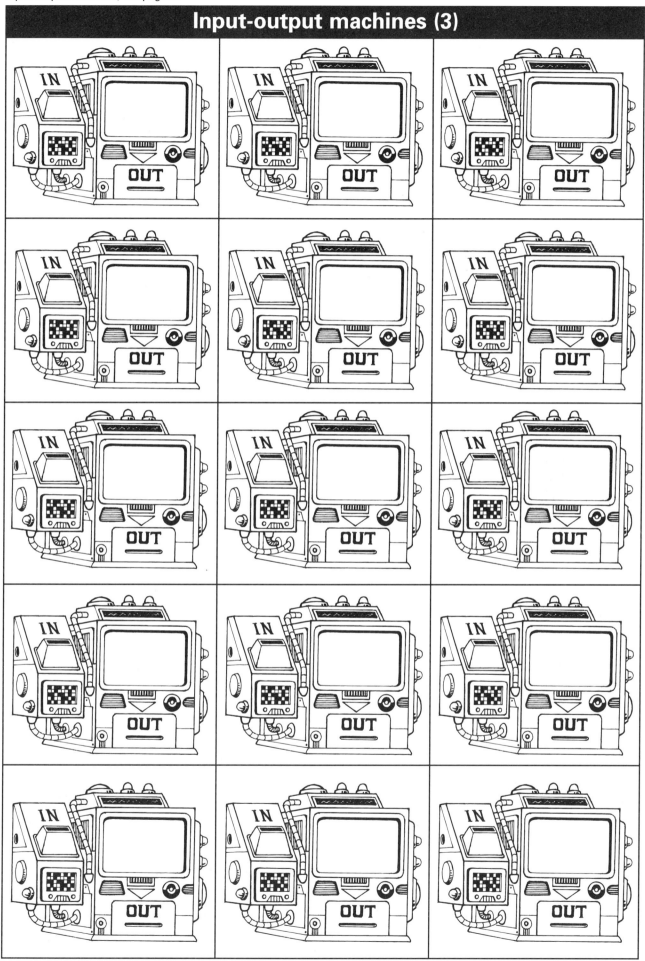

Pentominoes on a 100-square

1 Make any pentomino and place it on a 100 square.
Work out the total of the five numbers it is covering.

Move the pentomino one square to the right.
Work out the total of the five numbers.

What happens to the total when you move a pentomino one square to the right?

2 What happens to the total of the five numbers when you move a pentomino one square to the left?

3 What happens to the total of the five numbers when you move a pentomino one square up?

4 What happens to the total of the five numbers when you move a pentomino one square down?

5 What is the smallest total a pentomino can have?
Draw the pentomino and write the numbers in each square.

6 What is the biggest total a pentomino can have?
Draw the pentomino and write the numbers in each square.

7 Find a pentomino which has a total of exactly 100.
Draw the pentomino and write the numbers in each square.

8 Find a pentomino which has a total of exactly 200.
Draw the pentomino and write the numbers in each square.

NUMBER KEY STAGE TWO

The wall

Name _____   Date _____

Multiplication squares, see page 68

Multiplication squares

Name _____   Date _____

▲ Complete these multiplication squares.

x	2	5
3		
4		

x	4	7
3		
5		

x	2	10
5		
8		

x	7	10
6		
9		

x	4	8
7		
9		

x	5	9
6		
8		

▲ These multiplication squares show the answers.
You must work out the numbers being multiplied.

x		
	10	14
	20	28

x		
	6	30
	16	80

x		
	15	20
	18	24

x		
		36
	54	81

x		
	21	24
		40

x		
	24	
		24

▲ Try to complete the last square in more than one way.

The cardioid, see page 70

The cardioid

Name _____ Date _____

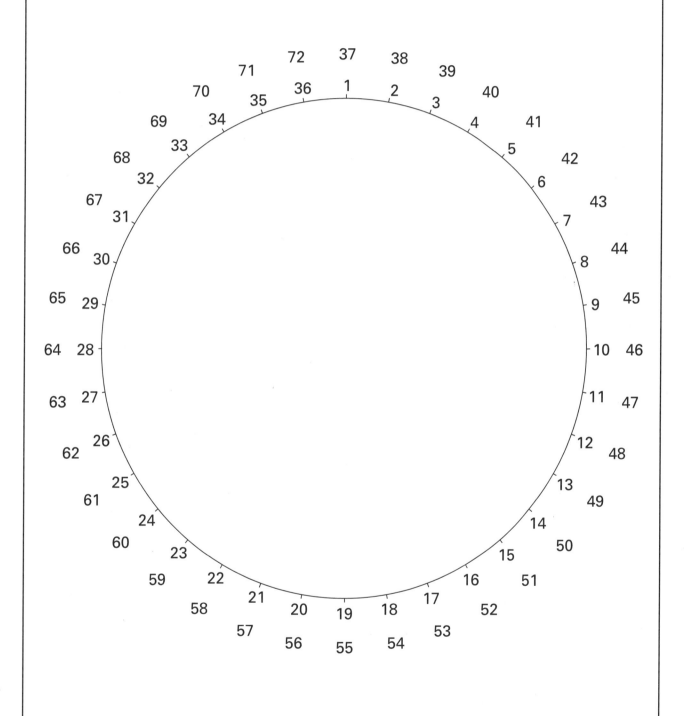

Estimating decimal multipliers, see page 74

Estimations (1)

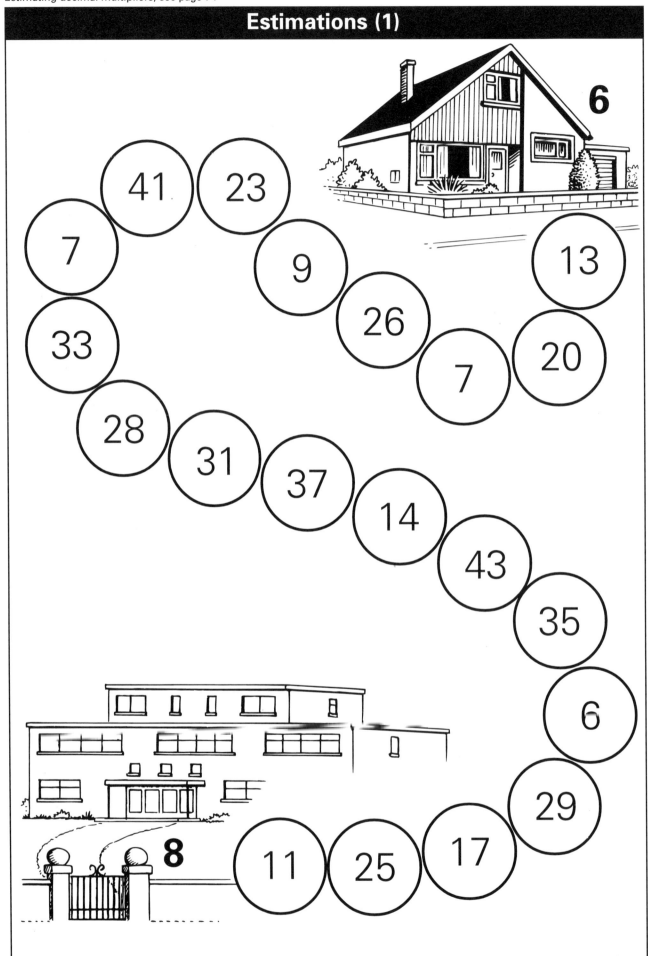

Estimating decimal multipliers, see page 74

Estimations (2)

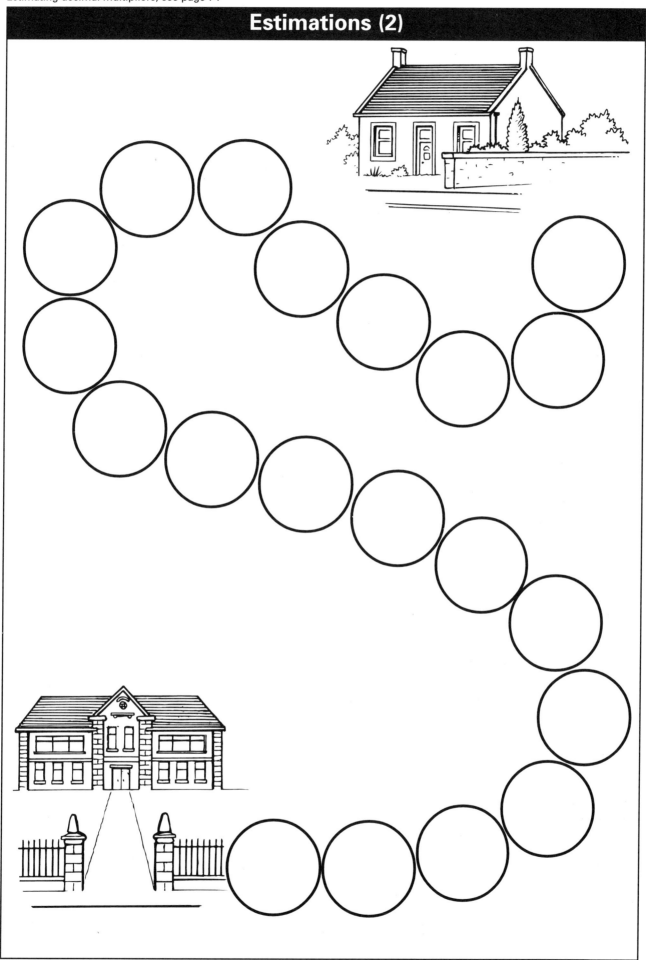

Remainders, see page 80

Remainders

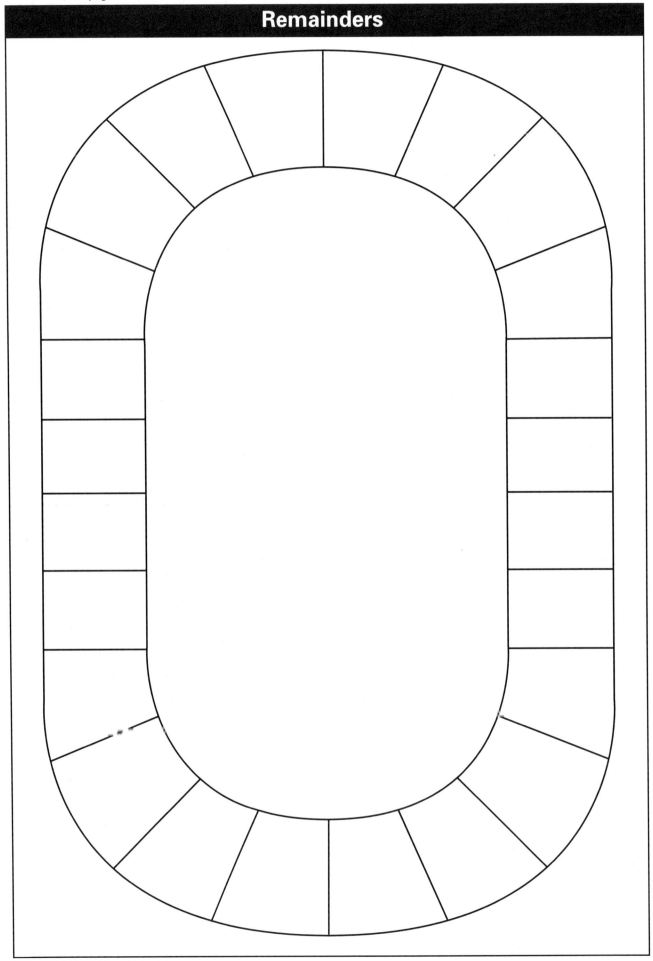

From 1 to 100, see page 82

From 1 to 100 (the first 50)

Name _____   Date _____

= 1		= 26
= 2		= 27
= 3		= 28
= 4		= 29
= 5		= 30
= 6		= 31
= 7		= 32
= 8		= 33
= 9		= 34
=10		= 35
= 11		= 36
= 12		= 37
= 13		= 38
= 14		= 39
= 15		= 40
= 16		= 41
= 17		= 42
= 18		= 43
= 19		= 44
= 20		= 45
= 21		= 46
= 22		= 47
= 23		= 48
= 24		= 49
= 25		= 50

From 1 to 100, see page 82

From 1 to 100 (the last 50)

Name _____   Date _____

	= 51		= 76
	= 52		= 77
	= 53		= 78
	= 54		= 79
	= 55		= 80
	= 56		= 81
	= 57		= 82
	= 58		= 83
	= 59		= 84
	= 60		= 85
	= 61		= 86
	= 62		= 87
	= 63		= 88
	= 64		= 89
	= 65		= 90
	= 66		= 91
	= 67		= 92
	= 68		= 93
	= 69		= 94
	= 70		= 95
	= 71		= 96
	= 72		= 97
	= 73		= 98
	= 74		= 99
	= 75		= 100

NUMBER KEY STAGE TWO

Three in a row

12	60	1	48	16	4	24
28	36	17	21	7	11	0
6	2	10	72	5	30	19
40	13	20	3	45	15	63
8	54	0	2	9	35	6
1	32	4	18	42	27	2
90	3	80	1	14	5	56

Three dice Bingo, see page 85

Three dice Bingo

Name _____ Date _____

1	2	3	4	5	6
7	8	9	10	11	12
13	14	15	16	17	18
19	20	21	22	23	24
25	26	27	28	29	30

Find..., see page 87

Find...

Remember, your numbers can be next to each other horizontally, vertically or diagonally.

1 Find two numbers next to each other that add up to

    20   30   35   48   77

2 Find two numbers next to each other that have a difference of

    2   9   15   20   32

3 Find three numbers next to each other in a line that add up to

    46   59   64   77   99

4 Find two numbers next to each other in a line that have a product of

    36   54   70   90   96

5 Find three numbers next to each other in a line that have a product of

    24   80   108   120   270

6 Find two numbers next to each other in a line that have a product of

    135   210   216   240   360

Times and dates, see page 91

Times and dates

1 Write down three times during the day when the hours and the minutes add up to 25.

2 Write down three times during the day when the hours and the minutes have a difference of 25.

3 Write down three times during the day when the hours and the minutes have a product of 50.

4 Write down three times during the day when the hours and the minutes have a product of 100.

5 What is special about 12th August 1920 and 20th October 1930?
When were the last three dates that this occurred?
When are the next three dates that it will occur?

6 What is special about 20th April 1916 and 25th May 1920?
When were the last three dates that this occurred?
When are the next three dates that it will occur?

7 What is special about 6th December 1972 and 8th November 1988?
When were the last three dates that this occurred?
When are the next three dates that it will occur?
Why are there no dates like this in 1997?

8 What is special about 30th March 1910 and 28th February 1914?
When were the last three dates that this occurred?
When are the next three dates that it will occur?